The Dream of Intelligence

THE DREAM OF INTELLIGENCE

SEBASTIAN BARKER

'I thought that the poet,
if he's going to be a poet,
should make fiction, not fact.'

Socrates, Plato: Phaedo

Littlewood Arc

First published in 1992
by Littlewood Arc
The Nanholme Centre
Shaw Wood Road
Todmorden Lancs OL14 6DA

Typeset by Lasertext
Stretford Manchester
Design and print by Tony Ward
at The Arc & Throstle Press
Todmorden Lancs OL14 6DA

ISBN 0 946407 80 0 hbk
0 946407 72 X pbk

Cover picture of
Waldlandschaft mit Bach und Steg
by Josef Anton Koch
(Tiroler Landesmuseum Ferdinandeum, Innsbruck)

ACKNOWLEDGEMENTS

Sitochorion, Trifillias, Messinias, Greece
Mount Pleasant, Reigate, Surrey
Ingram Merrill Foundation, New York, U.S.A.
Hawthornden Castle, Lasswade, Scotland
The Society of Authors
Harold Pinter
Peter & Diana Carter
The Brighton Festival
Dr. Geoffrey Edelsten
Dr. Keith Ansell-Pearson
Paul & Vivienne Kincaid
Dr. Arnab Banerji
Dr. Roy Macgregor
Jeremy Reed
Ralf Jeutter
transition, Göttingen, Germany
William & Patricia Oxley
Acumen, Brixham, Devon
Ioana Ieronim Brandus
Secolul 20, Bucharest, Romania
Radio Romania-Cultural
Walter Kaufmann
R.J. Hollingdale
J.P. Stern
Jill Simmonds

For Sally

Sure I dream as the hammer strikes the anvil,
And I dream as the sparks light on the floor . . .

Traditional Irish

While men the tragic poet's light resented,
The spirit that is Woman caressed his soul.

Patrick Kavanagh

. . . the problem of the origin of evil pursued me even as a boy of thirteen . . .

Friedrich Nietzsche

My resistance to the general slogan – 'We must present the drama and agony of our times' – is a deep one. When reality surpasses imagination in boldness, then poetic exaggeration becomes useless, and the affectation of pain becomes a mere coarsening of blood and tears. On the contrary, I think a poet must find those spiritual powers which may counterbalance this drama and this agony.

Odysseus Elytis

CONTENTS

PART THREE

NIETZSCHE IN HIS BED
DREAMING THE DREAM OF INTELLIGENCE,
Flat 3, 6 Via Carlo Alberto, Turin, Italy,
2nd January 1889, 11.45 p.m. Onwards

PART FOUR

THE AWAKENING,
Flat 3, 6 Via Carlo Alberto, Turin, Italy,
3rd January 1889, 7.00 a.m. Onwards

THE DREAM OF INTELLIGENCE

PART ONE

NIETZSCHE'S STUDY

Flat 3, Fourth Floor,
6 Via Carlo Alberto,
Turin,
Italy.

2nd January 1889
8.30 p.m.

CHAPTER 1

Nietzsche Pacing The Floor

Outside the streets are humming. Not far away, on the Via Po, students sit drinking beer under the arcades in the University quarter. Carriages stop by their tables, ladies and gentlemen alight, klaxons honk, spoked wheels splash through shallow puddles. Night will soon be upon us. A light rain will fall again.

What a noble city this is. Spacious streets, distinguished buildings. A man could live here. Everywhere columns, arches, arcades, wide-open squares. And those intriguing narrow back-streets, like the Via Barbarous, where bakers, midwives, grocers, now sit inside lit shops, keeping the night warm.

Down there in the Piazza Carlo Alberto cobbles ring with carriages, hand-pushed carts. The copper horse and horseman on their plinth, still glistening green from the rain, glow in the candelabra streetlamps. (*Opening a window*) Ah! what air this is! How good it is to breathe – after centuries of baroque, medieval fug. How I suffocated in those northern German cities, in the gloomy crypt of them all. Until I crossed the Alps.

Turin is a delight. Sophisticated people swagger and swank as they walk, shop, meet, glide to restaurants, illicit rendezvous.

But look at that man on the balcony opposite. He's searching the air in front of him for something to believe in, to cheer him up, but there's nothing. What hopelessness, what nothingness, seeing nothing has ever worked, nor ever will. And look how he proves the opposite of what he is thinking: for his people, the people of Turin, go on living all around him, as they have always done, immutable in the face of change. But he's too sad to see this, another victim of the Gorgon, pain.

Tonight when I dined in the Ristorante Peppino, I saw the same thing, but the other way round. I was sitting alone at a table when I felt a curious warmth coming from a table behind me on my right. I turned around unobtrusively and there was an entire Italian family congregated around three joined tables. I'd hardly noticed them come in, I'd been so engrossed in my own mind, but now to my astonishment, without knowing it, they were telling me something. Their conversation was down-key by Italian standards. They were talking among themselves with quiet intelligence. They were in truth, it seemed to me, nothing other than Turin. And Turin was nothing other than family life. Immutable in the very face of change. I felt a boundless gratitude. Such people were giving me back my life.

As I walked home, I stopped down there in the Piazza. I slipped off my shoes in the dark and felt the icy cobbles of the street below. For a moment, the ball of the world and I were petrified together. A tremor of delight slid through me. Why did I do this? I slipped on my shoes and hurried through the door of Number 6. The word 'Civilization' hit me like one I had been searching for but couldn't find. An awful contrast gripped me. I was released by the thought, 'It's *always* morality which makes life unbearable.'

Looking out on the Piazza now, the bright green grass under the streetlamps accepts without a murmur the heels of the couples on their way to dine. This is how it was this morning when I crossed the River Po, the mighty mountain tide rushing like angry pea soup under the Ponte Emmannele. I saw it, too, in the empty Franciscan churches, cavernous with gold under the dust and dirt. I saw that the poor people of Italy haven't changed in twenty centuries. The grand buildings degenerate to slums. Ghastliness lives side by side with beauty. The Italian artists in their youth set out to put it all to rights – only to perish in the snow.

And the bells of the Franciscan priory usher in the princes and the paupers, as the criminals and whores step back on the streets to let them enter.

What hope is there, faced with the scale of this challenge? What can anyone do? What can anyone ever do? And what about me? *I will complete my application for the Chair of Philosophy in Athens.* That's what I will do. I know it well, this giant of European Nihilism. *I will go to Athens. I will confront it there, inspired by the immortals.* As Confucius said, The way out is through the door.

CHAPTER 2

Nietzsche Writing At His Desk

Flat 3,
6, Via Carlo Alberto,
Turin,
Italy.

2nd January 1889

Professor Manolis Liakopoulos,
Department of Philosophy,
Athens University,
Akademias,
Athens,
Greece.

Dear Professor Liakopoulos,

I would like to apply for the post of Professor of Philosophy at Athens University, as advertised recently in the Italian press.

I enclose my *curriculum vitae* and other relevant papers.

Yours sincerely,

Professor Doctor
Friedrich Wilhelm Nietzsche

CHAPTER 3

Nietzsche Writing At His Desk

CURRICULUM VITAE

I was born on the 15th of October 1844 in the small farming village of Röcken in Saxony fifteen kilometres south-west of Leipzig. My father was a Protestant pastor and he had the living of the Röcken rectory. He was himself the son of a pastor. I was the eldest of three children. My father, Karl Ludwig, died when I was four. My younger brother, Joseph, died six months later. My sister, Elizabeth Thérèse Alexandra, survives.

At 7, I went to a private school. By 10, I had shown signs of ability. By 15, after the discipline of Schulpforta School near Naumburg, I was known as something of a scholar. By the time I left, although not outstanding in all subjects, I was accepted as the best pupil the School had ever had.

Between the ages of 15 and 18, I edited with two School friends, Wilhelm Pinder and Gustav Krug, the School literary magazine *Germania*. I contributed essays, short stories, and poems. In 1864, at the age of 20, I went to Bonn University, studying philology and theology. By Easter 1865, I'd given up theology. Later that year I transferred to Leipzig University.

My first published philological work, on the Greek poet Theognis, appeared in 1867 in *Das Rheinische Museum für Philologie* under the editorship of Professor Albrecht Ritschl. My second published work, on Greek philosophy, appeared in 1869 in *Literarisches Zentralblatt* under the editorship of Professor Friedrich Zarncke. The same year, 1869, I was appointed Professor of Classical Philology at Basle University in Switzerland. My duties also included Greek at the University's Grammar School. Leipzig University had by then awarded me my Doctorate, without examination. I was 24.

I'd been conscripted into the Mounted Field Artillery in the Prussian Army in 1867, but the University authorities in Basle saw fit to rescind this. A consequence of this was that I ceased to be a Prussian citizen. I've applied for Swiss citizenship, but as yet it hasn't come through. I gave public lectures at Basle University on 'Homer and Classical Philology', 1869, 'The Greek Music Drama', 1870, and 'Socrates and Tragedy', 1870, returning whenever possible to serve as a Medical Orderly in the Prussian Army. I caught diptheria and dysentery in the Medical Tents at Erlangen and was ordered back to Basle.

My first book, *The Birth of Tragedy out of the Spirit of Music*, was published by E.W. Fritzsch in Leipzig in 1872. I gave public lectures on 'The Future of our Educational Institutions', 1872, 'Philosophy during the Tragic Age of the Greeks', 1873, and 'On Truth and Falsehood in an Extramoral Sense', 1873.

Four essays published later under the title *Untimely Meditations* first appeared between 1873 and 1876. These were 'David Strauss the Confessor and Writer', E.W. Fritzsch 1873; 'On the Uses and Disadvantages of History for Life', E.W. Fritzsch 1874; 'Schopenhauer as Educator', Ernst Schmeitzner 1874; and 'Richard Wagner in Bayreuth', Ernst Schmeitzner 1876.

At this point in my career, I applied to the University for a sabbatical, which was granted. Later on, because of ill health, it was felt more appropriate that I should be given a pension. I was released from University duties to concentrate on my philosophical writings.

Human, All-Too-Human: A Book for Free Spirits was first published by Schmeitzner in spring 1878. I later added two collections of aphorisms, 'Assorted Opinions and Maxims', Schmeitzner 1879, and 'The Wanderer and his Shadow', Schmeitzner 1879, to make up a two-volume edition published by E.W. Fritzsch in 1886. *The Dawn: Thoughts on the Prejudices of Morality*, published by Schmeitzner, came out in July 1881.

This second stage in my career as a published writer ended with the publication of *The Gay Science*, Schmeitzner 1882.

I began the third and to date final stage of my writing career with the publication of *Thus Spoke Zarathustra* (Book One, Schmeitzner 1883; Book Two, Schmeitzner 1884; Book Three, Schmeitzner 1884; and Book Four, Privately Printed 1885).

This poem was a prelude to *Beyond Good and Evil*, C.G. Naumann 1886; *On the Genealogy of Morals*, C.G. Naumann 1887; and *Twilight of the Idols: How to Philosophise with a Hammer*, to be published by C.G. Naumann later this month.

I've also completed several other works, including 'The Case of Wagner', 'The Antichrist', 'Ecce Homo' (an autobiographical work), 'Nietzsche Contra Wagner', and 'Dithyrambs of Dionysus' (poetry).

My work as a whole was reviewed by Professor Karl Spitteler in the Bern *Bund* on 1st January 1888. In April 1888, Professor George Brandes gave a series of public lectures on my philosophy at Copenhagen University. He reported a widespread and appreciative response. Relevant press cuttings and a synopsis of Professor Brandes's lectures are enclosed.

CHAPTER 4

Nietzsche Pacing The Floor

What a drudge that was. Perhaps it will help? I'll post it off tomorrow from the Post Office in the Via San Francesco d'Assisi. The Chair, of course, could go to anyone, for any reason, such is the corruption in the academic world at the moment. But perhaps the Greeks are fairer about these things? I suspect they are, even if human nature varies so little.

If I am not given the Chair, at least I have the satisfaction of knowing there is no-one better qualified for it. In all conscience, is there anyone alive in the world more suitable?

Athens! The very name inspires. Sun and dust, sun and dust. No more gloom, no more German weight. No more rain, moss, lichen, fungus. Freedom to think. Money to endure. Ha! I'm getting sentimental. I must be getting tired. I'll go to bed.

PART TWO

NIETZSCHE IN HIS BED DREAMING THE DREAM OF DISASTER

Flat 3, Fourth Floor,
6 Via Carlo Alberto,
Turin,
Italy.

2nd January 1889
10.30 p.m.

CHAPTER 1

Nietzsche Asleep Dreaming He Is Alone In A Cab In Cologne 24 Years Earlier, 15th February 1865, Age 20¼

"Can you take me to 'a good restaurant'?"
"Certainly, Sir. Any particular kind?"
"You choose. I'll enjoy the view."
"Very well, Sir. You enjoy the view. I'll take you to 'a good restaurant'."
"You're very kind."
"Not at all. Have you come far?"
"Twenty kilometres."
"Quite a way."
"If you live here. I live in Bonn. I'm out for a day in Cologne. I'm a student at Bonn University."
"A student, eh? I'll see to you."
"You're very kind."
"Don't say that, Sir. You're paying for the cab."
"Of course. I forgot. I'm nervous."
"You nervous, Sir? Never. You're excited. You're a student, you said. Students tend to be polite – when they're sober."
"How far is it?"
"Not far. You sit back and enjoy the view."

CHAPTER 2

The Dream Continues In A Bar In Cologne That Night

"It was murder, Doctor Stringer, absolute murder. There I am, clanking over the cobblestones. The sun is jumping through the carriage windows. 'There it is,' says the cabman. We're in an eighteenth century street with terrace houses on either side. 'That's the one you want, Sir.' I felt as though I were dying. I felt as though I were riding into the womb 'embracing the secret motive of my sex'."

"Steady on, old chap. Don't overdo it."

"I know, I know. But I'm on my way to a brothel, and nothing in the world can stop me. What a feeling. I'll bet you can remember it yourself. And the sweet complicity of the cabman, just as I'd been told."

"A brothel? What do I know about brothels?"

"Quite a lot, I suspect, Doctor Stringer."

"You're right there. Another schnapps?"

"Just fill it up. So there I am, outside paying the cabman. What a tactful old dolt he was. Do you know, he turned the other way to cough? Why do you think he paid me that compliment?"

"Probably just habit. I think you're more than a little drunk."

"We're both drunk, Doctor. Why did he pay me that compliment?"

"Perhaps he didn't condemn you?"

"Right. He condoned me. He condoned us all."

"All right, so he was a sweet chappie. What did you say the brothel was called?"

"The Manchunia Hotel."

"Quite a mouthful, when you're drunk. At least you can still pronounce it."

"He left me leaning against the black, rusty railings. I was staring at the peeling walls. There was dust on the black paint on the railings. I touched the dust, marvelling at it. So this is it, I was thinking, dust and all."

"Fetching. Was this your first sexual experience?"

"I wouldn't say that. I wouldn't say that at all, Doctor Stringer. Let's just say – let's just drink to Silka and her friends. Shall we rise . . . ?"

"Sit down. Why are you so evasive? You don't have to be sentimental with me."

"I'm sorry. I promised to tell you the truth, didn't I?"

"It doesn't matter. But I wouldn't put it past you."

"Doctor Stringer, Doctor Leonard Stringer, you are what you describe as 'an enlightened English doctor'. You say you're here in Cologne working on research at the neurological hospital. I think you're a womaniser and a drunk. You happen to be feeling whimsical tonight, so, to make a change, you pick up a half-drunk student, out for the day in the big city, and get him drunker. Why? He's just come out of a brothel, The Manchunia Hotel – see, I said it again – and you're so bloody nosey and jaded you want to hear all the details. Isn't that right? Isn't that the truth?"

"That's the spirit! Of course. The fact is, I'm a bit lonely. I'm in a foreign city, a long way from home, and you looked better company than the average whore or one more bloated burgher."

"So you're using me?"

"So? *You're* using *me*."

"Touché. You're honest, Doctor Stringer, that's what I like about you. So why do you want to know about my sex life? Will it advance the cause of neurology?"

"Of course it will, old boy. All right, let's make peace. Don't tell me everything. Just the facts about this afternoon."

"Was that what I promised in the other bar?"

"Yes. But let's not dwell on it. The facts."

"It was late afternoon. The sun was setting at the end of Mittelstrasse. I was climbing the steps to the front door . . . "

". . . and . . "

"If I said I was a controlled jelly negotiating its way to the bell . . . "

"I'd believe you. Get on with it."

"I was terrified. The boozy boastings of my students' union, The Frankonia, were ringing in my ears, needling me on. The trouble was, the more I crept forward, the more my will weakened. I kept hearing their brash words, cruelly exposing their virginity. Now it was my turn, wavering on the steps, wishing I were back there, but drawn irresistibly to the bell."

"Don't tell me you funked it?"

"I pressed the bell all right. I waited an age. Then, slowly, the door opened. I began to feel like nothing at all . . . like a transparency of the world itself gently trembling in the breeze. 'Take me in, take me in,' I was praying. I couldn't stand it anymore."

"Risky stuff."

"Right. A dignified woman in her fifties opened the door. We stood for a moment looking at each other. She had beautiful grey hair. 'May I take your coat?' she said, holding out her finely manicured hands. I took off my coat and gave it to her."

"Was she in charge?"

"No. She was the Receptionist. There was something respectable about her. Perhaps that's why they employed her? She sat down behind her desk and with a sweet smile indicated the door I had to pass through."

"A courteous lady."

"She gave me back my strength. I pushed open the door and walked in, closing the door behind my back. The room was dark. I wanted to get used to the light."

"I know the feeling."

"There were about a dozen women in the room, and two

men. I noticed satin, lace, and red velvet curtains. There was a bar on the left with the two men and five of the women. They were sitting on stools drinking. The other women were loosely assembled around a big table on the right. A weary chandelier hung from the ceiling. My back was frozen to the door. More than a dozen pairs of eyes pinned me there, scrutinizing me. Having no malice myself, I felt none coming back at me. This made me feel a crumb of gratitude. Straight ahead on the opposite side of the room I saw a grand piano, a majestic island of black and shiny safety. To get to it I had to pass under the chandelier, exposing myself to the light. But at least I knew what to do when I got there. There was nothing else in the room I understood."

"So you plucked up courage and walked across?"

"'Walked' is being too kind. I strode across, absurdly conscious of my absurdity. I heard titters. 'The music, get to the music', I was thinking. I sat on the piano stool, opened the keyboards, and struck several chords, moderately loud, to tell them I knew how absurd I was. Then I began playing a melody, a new one, not yet widely known, but moving and delicate. I knew at once they hadn't heard it. Slowly the atmosphere was turning from insult to fascination. Music had broken the spell. Several of the ladies on the right glided towards me. As I played, I knew I was no longer the centre of attention in the room. Normality had returned. I had been absorbed. I even had a couple of admirers watching my hands on the keyboard."

"So what happened next?"

"One of them put a glass of wine on the piano clearly intended for me. I scented several perfumes around me, and felt four proud minds searching every move I made. They knew what I was doing. They knew what I was saying with my music."

"And what might that have been?"

"That I respected their dignity."

"Dignity in a brothel. Are you joking?"
"Dignity in a brothel. Just as I say. Their bad teeth, their foul tempers, the ugliness – you can keep all that. The rotten side of life was well out of sight. It was dawning on me, in fact, that I'd come at a good time. They were all full of energy, of curiosity. They knew I was intrigued by them even before I'd looked at them. One of them purred in my ear, 'Why don't you come and join us when you've finished playing?' How could I resist that? I smiled and kept on playing. When I reached the end of the piece, I picked up the glass and went over to their table."
"The big round one on the right?"
"The big round one on the right. It was draped with a heavy cream lace table-cloth. I bowed my head and smiled modestly as I sat down, and all at once a kind of warm commotion broke out."
"What do you mean, 'a warm commotion'? Did you wet your knickers? I mean, what happened?"
"I don't know. Perhaps my music had broken a taboo? Whatever it was, the thin film between prostitute and client had disappeared. A kind of excited chatter started up. There was a sudden evaporation of formality. I heard a knowing sigh or two from the women at the bar, the older ones. I suppose those of us at the table simply reverted to what we were: eight young people in a strange and exciting place. After all, I was outnumbered seven to one. They had nothing to fear from a twenty year old boy. They could afford to relax. This sort of thing didn't happen every day."
"Just every so often."
"And why not? There obviously wasn't much trade. The girls took the chance. They called over to the bar for several jugs of wine. This was going to be an afternoon in which *they* had a little fun. The brawny old Madam behind the bar gave them the nod. What worried me was the part I was supposed to play."
" 'Prostitutes' pet?"

"That's what I was thinking. I was stroked, cajoled into smiling, and softened up with a few risqué jokes. Would I get up and flee? Or did I have the staying power to keep them amused? I must say, they exercised restraint until they knew I was going to stay. This didn't take long. I'd already told myself I'd pretend to my friends I'd left after the piano incident. Now I knew that I was welcome I felt in a secret time of my own."

"I can't say I blame you. What did you do now? Drink?"

"We drank all right. Three times the jugs were refilled. I'd never seen young women drink so much. I drank with them glass for glass. It was intoxicating. Not so much the drink, though that helped, but the uncanny air of subterranean manners. They liked subverting my formal respectability, then substituted it with their own. We all found this very enjoyable."

"I see you're no prig. Tell me, who were they exactly? What kind of people were they?"

"A bit too innocent for you, Doctor, I'd say. These girls were in their early twenties, like me. Most of their sophistication was put on, like their seductive dresses and costume jewelry. But that is precisely what I liked about them. They were like me, but the opposite sex. I suppose you could say I was meeting some of my peers."

"I think this schnapps is making you soft. Since when did a table of prostitutes merit equal rank with a student?"

"Since forever, Doctor. You haven't just spent all your life locked up in a school with other boys. You have forgotten how wonderful it is, how *innocent* it is, to see people without moral prejudice. You're the one who's going soft."

"Possibly, quite possibly. So there you were, in a nice little social get-together – in a brothel."

"So? It *was* a brothel – we all knew that. That was part of the fun. The great thing was no one was in a hurry. We had all the time in the world."

"I bet your brawny old Madam had her eye on the clock."

"Of course she did. We all did. You've missed the point."
"Which was?"
"We'd noticed as a group that for a while at least we were ahead of time. You must have noticed this yourself? Sometimes events conspire against the tick-tock of the dreary old grandfather clock in the corner. We can be happy for a while."
"*You're* telling *me*? I must be getting old."
"No, Doctor, just drunk."

*

"You're telling me you got special treatment. I'm telling you you're boasting."
"I'm telling you the truth. I was lucky."
"You're flattering yourself."
"Am I? The truth is, Doctor, you're jealous. You're feeling past it. I had a wonderful time, and so did they. It was all very witty, very silly, very crass – and quite wonderful."
"Don't you wish you were back there, instead of sitting here with an old, drunken, jealous reprobate?"
"Come now, Leonard, you're not that bad. I *liked* them. That was all. It was only Silka, the one on my left, who got close to me."
"Silka was special?"
"We got on straight away. She was the one who stood behind me at the piano, whispering, 'Why don't you come and join us?' She read me like a book. She put me at my ease."
"What about the others?"
"Silka introduced us. I suppose you could say Silka was an ordinary blonde. But the closer she sat, the less ordinary she seemed to me. She had on nothing more than a white lace slip beneath a maroon satin dressing-gown. When she looked at me through her soft blue eyes, I could have sworn she had fallen for me the day before. How could I resist

that? She had on no make-up, except thick red lipstick which mocked itself. She put her hand on my knee after her first glass of wine. She went round the table, clockwise."

*

"Quite a table. So what happened?"
"As I said, I was always with Silka, from the moment she looked at me. Something in her attracted me. Her compassion, probably. I felt safe in her company. We enjoyed each other."
"She sounds a good woman."
"She was. Well, anyway, after a decent interval, when we were all fairly drunk, she took me to her room. It was as simple as that. Everyone noticed that as we left the table we smiled simultaneously. We went out a back-door and down a dimly-lit corridor.
"Once in her room, she undressed me, starting with my tie and collar. There was nothing to it. I felt so at ease in her company, there was nothing but delight in everything that followed. I gave myself up to her. She felt a little of the same, I think, judging by her expression. I don't think it was just the drink, nor was she entirely mercenary. She kept looking out of her big blue soulful eyes, as though she was in my power, when all-too-evidently it was the other way round.
"Once on her bed, and naked, she took me into herself as if we had been born to do so."
"Lucky bastard."
"That's what I thought. She enclosed and consoled the violence of my passion as though I would always be welcome in her bed. We were two hours together. Can it be possible all this happened today? That was Silka of The Manchunia Hotel, Silka the gentle-eyed."
"I wish all visits to brothels were as happy."
"Afterwards, when we were dressed, she held my hand and

led me down the corridor. She ordered two wines. 'Where are the others?' 'Working.' The evening had begun. Full bellies followed by guilty faces ambled in. It was not difficult to see the disgust the women held back against the human race. For them, there was no salvation, not even the fool's paradise of drink.

"We chinked glasses. She was indulging me, even a little bored. I had, after all, turned back into a strait-laced young man. I was beginning to fall out of love with the place. Silka put down her glass. We walked without holding hands to the exit. 'You're a beautiful man,' she said, 'don't ever get discouraged.' She gave me a little wet kiss on the lips. 'You will be there, behind everything I do,' I promised extravagantly. 'I know', she said, surprising me. 'Goodbye.' 'Goodbye,' I echoed her. She closed the door.

"I nodded to the Receptionist. Once out the front door, I sucked in the frosty night air of Cologne, jubilant in the lamplit street, here in the middle of a gruesome German winter."

"And you went to the first bar you could find and got drunker?"

"What else was there to do? Ah yes, of course, and then I met you, Doctor, no stranger to wine and whorehouses yourself. You were out on your own little binge."

"True enough. We doctors have a duty to experience the world – just like you young theology students."

"That's what they all say."

"And they're right, too, aren't they? Come on, you well-dressed little fuss-pot, drink up."

*

"I've just had a thought."

"Which is?"

"What if Silka had syphilis?"

"I do believe you're having an attack of conscience. You'll

certainly find out if she did. Look on the bright side."
"Perhaps the sweetness of our afternoon has condemned us both to insanity and death?"
"Oh for Christ's sake, man, don't be so gloomy. It's so German, so boring."
"Is that all you can say? I suppose you're right."
"Silka doesn't sound like the syphilitic type to me."
"I'm sorry. I'll get over it. I feel as though I've just signed my own death warrant."
"That's your conscience you're feeling. Get used to it."
"You're right. I keep going to extremes. Let's toast Silka."
"To Silka."
"To Silka the gentle-eyed."
"Let's get drunk."
"You're the doctor."

*

CHAPTER 3

The Dream Continues In The Streets Of Turin 24 Years Later, Age 44¼

"Doctor Stringer! I thought I'd never see you again."
"Good God, it's the theology student. What are you doing in Turin?"
"I gave up theology. I became a Professor of Philology. I've just been appointed Professor of Philosophy at Athens University. I'm sailing in three weeks."
"Goodness me. Many congratulations."
"Can you believe it?"
"To look at you? Yes."
"Brilliant, isn't it?"
"It calls for a celebration. Champagne. You must come to my house. I've got a magnificent place nearby. I've got a practice too. I'm a reformed character."
"You look it. What happened to the wine and the whore-houses?"
"I put all that behind me. I came to respect my profession too much to go on addling my brains. But I'll never make it to being a prude. Come on, let's have a drink. To celebrate old times."
"I don't drink very much."
"Nonsense, Professor. Don't hide behind your spectacles and that magnificent Tamarin monkey moustache. We all drink when we have to, and this is such a time. It is irreverent not to honour the past."
"Very well. We'll go to your house."
"Courage, Professor, that's the stuff. Come, we'll light a fire. Now tell me, how did the world turn? How did you get on after your student days?"
"I wrote books. I published nine books."
"On?"

"The turning world!"
"Of course."
"I'll tell you the details later. How did you come to have a practice in Turin? What happened to England? To Germany?"
"I've always loved Italy and the Italians. One day, through my German colleagues, I heard of this practice. How could I resist it? Italy is one of my passions. Everything was under one roof."
"And you never married?"
"You're joking of course. I'm a born bachelor. To the house, man, to the house."

*

"Silka did have syphilis."
"Oh my God."
"After that visit to The Manchunia Hotel – two years after, to be precise – I spent a lot of time visiting two doctors in Leipzig. They made it clear I'd got syphilis. There was a possibility it was an hereditary form, although this was extremely unlikely. There was a possibility I had caught it from early sexual experiences with either sex; even young boys, they assured me. There was a possibility, in other words, that I had not caught it from Silka – the point was unprovable – but from someone else. Whatever the case, I was doomed.
"They were terribly polite. But there was no use pretending they were saying anything else. They had clearly spoken in such a way many times before. 'There is no point in sugaring the pill. You've got syphilis. The incubation period can be short – a few years – or long – over twenty years. I'm sure you know as well as we do the disease is virtually incurable. If anyone could cure you, we would. But the truth is, there is little we can do. The wisest thing you can do, in the circumstances, is to tell your family and friends you're being

treated for an obscure nervous disorder. *Never* mention the word syphilis.' The doctors confirmed what I had suspected for some time. Silka did have syphilis. All the same, I came out of there a shaken man. I was 22 years old. All I had to look forward to was insanity and death. Just as I'd feared that very night.

"I looked up everything in the textbooks, of course, before the first symptoms arrived. I studied every significant work on the subject. I knew everything there was to know about syphilis, except how to cure myself. I realised at once this creature had a life and right to exist of its own. I wasn't going to get caught in the trap of projecting my disappointment and my fury against life onto a worm. But the fact was, such worms were eating Silka and myself alive. I formed a picture of the horror of life I've never lost."

"How can you be so sure it was Silka? Surely you've visited other prostitutes? And what about those young boys in Italy you used to eulogise?"

"Doctor Stringer, I went back to The Manchunia Hotel. I asked after Silka. I became friends with the Receptionist, the grey-haired Mathilde Helgar. She knew what I was getting at, she knew how concerned I was about Silka. But Silka had left the Hotel. She knew that Silka was being treated, but she couldn't or wouldn't tell me where. She made it clear that Silka wouldn't want to see someone she'd infected...I was looking into the profound horror of existence, I can tell you. I'd been haunted by it since I was 13, and here it was inside me."

"That young?"

"That young. I saw now I was in the same position as anyone else, as any normal, healthy person. Life itself, it now seemed so obvious, was nothing other than a fatal or incurable disease. 'No one gets out of life alive.' Syphilis made me see that the sword of death had already entered me. Could this be turned to advantage? After the shock,

I felt so alive."

"Did you consider suicide?"

"Suicide is one of the single greatest temptations of the soul. And yes, I was tempted. It looks like the easy way out. But I had also been tempted by something greater: philosophy. Of what use was suicide to me?"

"Not even to kill the pain? To prevent worse pain?"

"Ah, Doctor Stringer, now you talk of pain. I do not believe suicide is the way out of pain. It annihilates pain all right, but life and philosophy as well, and for that reason must be resisted!"

"So what is your prescription, Professor, if you will excuse my gentle mockery? What are you going to do about the fact that you are dying of syphilis? And what do you have to say to all the other people in the world suffering from incurable diseases like leprosy and life? How do you square your pious good will with the suffering in the world at large? Aren't you just another dreamer? Surely you can understand the snarling disgust your high-minded attitude to pain causes people?"

"You speak well, Doctor. What I have to tell you is nothing contemptible, if a man's life means anything to you, as it so clearly does. For what I have to tell you is the story of my life. Nothing less is worthy of you, for the story of my life, now that I have so little left, has become my philosophy."

"So how do we survive a fatal disease?"

"Don't be so impatient. Don't murder thought even before its inception. How long have we got?"

"We've got all night."

"We'll need it. For this is the story of the triumph of my philosophy over insanity and death."

"You're joking of course."

"You will be the judge of that."

"There are twelve logs here by the fire, Herr Professor. Each time there's a long pause in your story, or an obvious break, I'll get up and put another log on the fire. Do you think there are enough logs there? Or shall I fetch some more?"

"Those should see us through."

"Are you sure?"

"I'm sure."

"All right, so tell me about yourself. But please remember, this is not a conversation. Don't expect me to say anything. I will listen, I am all ears, but I will say nothing. I am here neither to agree nor to disagree with anything you say. I am a physician, not a dialectician. Come, the night is yours. Tell me the story of your life."

PART THREE

NIETZSCHE IN HIS BED DREAMING THE DREAM OF INTELLIGENCE

Flat 3, Fourth Floor,
6, Via Carlo Alberto,
Turin,
Italy.

2nd to 3rd January 1889
11.45 p.m. onwards

The Dream of Intelligence: 1

To justify our slow decline from grace
We draw on any product of the mind,
This reason, that experience, this fact,
To embed it over and against life.
Struck dumb in the glut of death, the blood and hair,
The instinct for rhythmic relationships
Alone provides the bearings which inspire.
Rhythm is like a bridge. It spans the gap
Between the establishment and vision.
Geared to the mud, yet tossed in airborne steel,
An acrobat in stern geometry,
A bridge, in fact, is objective rhythm.
Objective rhythm is what my life's about
Now my forty-fourth birth has come and gone
For, as you'll see, my story is a bridge.

One perfect day, when every fruit was ripe,
The grapevine sagged, and sunlight tanned my page,
I checked the stock of all I had achieved
And weighed it in the balance. I had won
The title of the right to slip the dross
Of what I was to death, released forever
From the gruesome tyranny of effort.
A man destined for immortality
Finds 'threescore years and ten' a witty joke.
For him, there is nothing more than the moment
In which to give up his entire being
To life. *There is nothing left to bury,*
The dross is consigned to mortality.
What lives on is his essential being,
A truth, a work of rare enlightenment,

The fruit of all he's done in honest labour.
With nine books published, and five in manuscript,
Why should I not feel gratitude to life?
   I sing the philosophy of Dionysus,
The reason-melting power of the heart.
Plato used Socrates like this, to forge
A semiotic of the holy life.

2

When I was four, my father died, and then
My little brother Joseph. I was dead.
Happiness and joy, like a summer's day,
Vanished, cracked to thunder, the clinker skies
Stabbed lightning through the roof, and through my bed.
My mother's grief ripped walls. I heard her cry
Ludwig is dead and now my baby boy.
Those days were long. We wept. We more than wept,
Earthly remains entrusting to the earth.
Oh the tolling of those bells in Röcken now
Shall I forget them, Leonard? Shall I forget
The tolling of those bells in Röcken now?
Oh I think not my darling my darling
Father and brother to their clangour gone.
The gloomy melody inside that church
Chanting '*Jesu meine Zuversicht*', I swear
I have never heard a more hollow sound.
   Karl Ludwig was thirty-six, Joseph two.
Franziska, my mother, was obliged to quit
The Rectory at Röcken Karl had made
A paradise on earth in all our lives,
For Karl's successor, that lifeless April
In 1850 when I crawled to school.

3

We moved to Naumburg – on the River Saale –
Still then walled, the gates being shut at ten

To open in the dark at 5 a.m.
  And there I lived until my fourteenth year
Mixing with few, but passionate with some
Like Wilhelm Pinder, at whose father's house
I first heard Goethe; like Gustav Krug, whose home
Was host to music and musician's talk.
  Nobody was surprized when I was given
A free place at the local boarding-school,
Schulpforta, famous throughout Germany,
Like Rugby in England: a self-contained
Precincts of sandstone buildings, one of which
Had an observatory in the roof.
  The precincts closed an academic world
Of ancient trees, a duck pond, quiet walks
Beyond the church the size of a cathedral.
I liked it there. I liked the high standards.
I liked the beat of the heart of Europe,
Of European civilization.
And I worked. Flowers bloomed outside the classroom,
But industry was furious within.

4

For some time, before my father was called
The Pastor of Röcken, he lived in a castle
At Altenburg, and taught four Princesses:
One of whom is now Queen of Hanover,
One The Duchess Constantin, one The Duchess
Of Oldenburg, and one Princess Thérèse
Of Saxé-Altenburg. He loved the King,
Friedrich Wilhelm the Fourth, who honoured him
With the Pastorate at Röcken. I was born
On the King's birthday, October the 15th
1844, and, as is fitting,
Given the Hohenzollern names *Friedrich Wilhelm.*
All my childhood my birthdays were holidays.
  I was blessed to have had such a father.

Because of him, I feel no loss of nerve
Entering the sophisticated worlds
Of delicate and elevated manners.
I am at home there. My innermost passions
Are free at last. And ah, what freedom is.

5

I was a studious boy, not bookwormy,
Though short sight forced me to wear glasses
From the age of 6, which embarrassed me
In gangs, fights, and games. But I liked swimming,
Skating, and hiking through the countryside.
I was physically strong, not the weakling,
To look at me now, you see I have become.
The Spartan discipline of Schulpforta
Started a 4 a.m. Classes at 6
Continued till 12. At 1.15
We began again, stopping at ten to 4.
Then more evening classes and bed at 9
Five days a week. On Saturdays we stayed
An extra hour in bed, then spent the day
Revising the week's work. Sundays were free.
I knew the nausea of homesickness.
The curriculum of the school was built
Around Latin and Greek. We breathed the air
Of Rome and Athens – and the Germany
Of Goethe and Schiller. Mathematics
And the sciences were taught – in their place.
I learned Hebrew, to help theology,
But never mastered the grammar. I read
Shakespeare and Byron, but in translation.
I dabbled in Italian. And French
I dipped into with a dictionary.
At 19, I hiked my hide to Kösen
With a wry mate called Richter. We got drunk
In the railway station – and caught red-handed

By a scandalized teacher. I was stripped
Of my status as a prefect hey ho
And somewhat shocked, but not seriously.
  Seventeen months later, I left the school.
Farewell was sad. My school valediction,
Spoken in Latin, was on Theognis
Of Megara: an original Essay
In the hard science of philology.
Farewell was sad. After our last goodbye,
Promising to remember each other,
I wrote a poem, *To The Unknown God.*

6

Next month I entered the University
Of Bonn: a student of philology
(The philosophical study of language)
And theology, which I abandoned.
(I'll pass over the trip to the brothel.)
Ten months later, I transferred to Leipzig.
  Where, one fine day in a secondhand bookshop,
I picked up a book by Schopenhauer
Called, *The World as Will and Idea.* I
Toyed with it, as something foreign to me,
Turning the pages slowly. 'Take it home,'
A demon whispered in my ear. Once home,
I threw myself on the sofa, and read,
And read and read and read and read and read.
That mighty intellect was a mirror
Of terrifying grandeur, in which I saw
This life, this world, and my own nature, back.
Here was health, and sickness, exile, refuge,
Radiance, death, hell, and heaven itself.
  I was a university student
Studying under Professor Ritschl,
One of the bright stars of philology.
One fine day, I arranged to visit him,

Feeling the need for critical comment
On the revised manuscript of my Essay.
He took me in. Stunned, he said he'd seen,
In a student in his first summer term,
Nothing to compare with my Theognis.
I saw that he was shocked and that I was
From that moment on born a philologist.
Ritschl was so impressed, and so impressed
His colleagues at Leipzig, he was able,
When the right moment came, to secure me
The newly-vacant Basle Professorship,
The Chair of Classical Philology,
At 24. This was a sensation.
My personal feelings towards the Chair,
To tell you the truth, were ambiguous.
Sometimes I hated it, deprecating
The crabbed study of dead books. The divine
Can-can and the yellow poison absinthe
Were more the subjects of my interest.
But I had the Chair. For the next 10 years
My nose was to the grindstone. And I worked.

7

But the seed of Schopenhauer had taken,
As I was well aware. Deep in my blood
His influence was spreading. Wings of fire
Were beating on a tender Phoenix there
Brooding her immortal philosophy.
I had found my life, and now I lived it
In the one hope of saving my own soul,
And all afflicted people, who, like me,
Know what it is to be doomed. Redeemed by art,
The science of religion, and the love,
Erupt full-grown, Sweet Music, lift your soul
Out of the flames and ashes of damnation
Ruptured at last of its most precious gold.

8

In practice, of course, it is typical
Of philosophy, throughout its history,
That such respect for beauty *and* horror,
Such love for creation *and* destruction,
Such veneration, *because of love*, for life,
Is the one thing philosophy abhors.
It is this very point, nevertheless,
Which is the vital distinguishing mark
Of Dionysian philosophy:
This love, which foresees pain and violence,
Yet still concurs with life; this love, which looks
Profoundly into horror as it is,
And joy, to redeem them as they are;
This love is *the wisdom of tragedy*
The God Apollo called Dionysian.
Plato used Socrates like this, to forge
A semiotic of the holy life.

The Dream of Intelligence:2

My most important household God is food.
That's what a person wants. What will I eat?
Will I die of exposure or starve first?
How can I stay healthy if I eat grass?
Who can say he's a new Renaissance man
Dining on odious moral cabbage,
Pedagogic mustard, and flatulent wine?
  I used to eat genuine Christian food
Twenty years ago with my fellow students.
Yet, in reality, all this meant was
We sat in a long cold refectory
Wolfing down spoonfuls of Christmas pudding
Earnestly suppressing the urge to scream.
  My next most vital household God is drink.
Alcohol. One glass of good wine or beer
Each day, however, is enough for me.
To suppose excess would make me cheerful
I would have to think like the Christians.
Nevertheless, while moderate amounts
Make me dizzy, I can take a large dose
Every so often, though I recognise
The authentic core of my character
Abstains from alcohol altogether.
Water douses the visionary fire,
Alcohol's grossly inflammatory.
To me, in fact, the stone drinking fountain
Found in a leafy street or city park
Is the hallmark of civilization.
In vino veritas? I don't believe it.
What a miserable idea of truth!
But I am ready to give it a try.

And a little strong tea in the morning.
To sit down as seldom as possible,
Crediting nothing not born in the air,
A man healthy, eating and drinking well,
Walking alone through the wild countryside –
That is my idea of trapping insight.

2

Next in my pantheon with food and drink
The principal Gods are place and weather.
They also affect the metabolism.
Genius in some way may well depend
On the physiological balance
Of these four Gods. Why do Jerusalem,
Athens, Florence, Provençe, Paris, London,
Stimulate the arts in different ways?
Why do wit, malice, elegance, happiness,
Flourish or die? Because of the climate!
Dry air, blue sky, a good metabolism,
These are, for me, the known preconditions
To unleash the terrifying energies
Necessary in any work of art.
It isn't because I had no close friends
I have no nostalgia for childhood.
I had no true friends then and I've none now.
Don't patronise or pity me for this.
The serenity of childhood wonder
Exalts me here on the streets of Turin.
And why? Because of the place, the climate.
Once out of the debilitating fog
Of Naumburg, Schulpforta, Leipzig, and Basle,
And settled in Turin, my sluggishness,
My morbidity, vanished completely.
I could work. I would work at the work
I was born to do – and relish the thought.
So how did I become a philologist?

Why didn't I take up a useful job,
Like a doctor or surgeon or someone
Skilled in making practical objects?
Why did I become a philologist?
I blame it on the weather. Like my friends,
I went careering down the dark valley
Of life in northern Germany, too white,
Too ill, too sick, to see the cul-de-sac:
The one-way street to the house of the dead.
  I was shocked to learn how stupid I was.
It was only when I was nearly dead,
In the strict physiological sense,
That I realised what a fool I'd been.
Of course! *Food, wine, sunlight, burnished cities!*

3

So what is my next most important God?
Leisure. The creative use of leisure.
Take reading. But as a genuine pleasure,
Not something done for work or money.
It liberates us. We meet strange people,
Strange science, yet take none of it to heart.
  When I work, I never have books with me;
Nor can I bear talk or people thinking.
If, by accident, I pick up a book,
This creates exactly the same effect:
I am cut to the quick by someone's mind.
It is absolutely vital to me
To be in retreat from human contact,
And this includes books of every kind.
Solitude is one of the wise instincts
Of the soul. To allow haphazard thoughts
Floating out of books or conversations
To intrude, betrays a frivolity
In the fundamental mood of the mind.
(I know. I've suffered it often enough.)

So what about favourite books? German ones?
I haven't read a German book in six months.
As a rule, I re-read the same authors,
The exceptions, the ones who've passed the test
Of cogency and relevance to life.
I don't admire wide or captious reading
Unregulated by a point of view.
Reading rooms make me feel slightly seasick,
And new books make me cautious, even sly.
I'm fond of the old Frenchmen, like Pascal,
Though I can't really read him anymore.
His books, frankly, cause me too much pain.
Pascal's life, to me, is one of the few
Most horrible, heart-breaking sights I know
In the entire history of loss of soul.
First psychological, then physical
Capitulation: the stark self-sacrifice
Of one of the finest minds in Europe
To a willed blindness: Christianity.
I find myself weeping to watch him light
That pyre of intellectual kindling
Under the living body of knowledge,
All for the sake of Christian dogma.
Few other facts distress me so deeply.
Then there's Montaigne. I love his wantonness.
My instinctive preference in the arts
Inclines me to Moliére, Racine, Corneille.
I'd defend any one of them against
The disorderly genius of Shakespeare.
I don't say I don't like modern Frenchmen
Like de Maupassant and Anatole France.
In fact, I prefer their generation
To the one before – Taine, for example –
Pulverized by German philosophy.
Does anything of Taine survive Hegel?
As far as Germany extends, it ruins culture.

Stendhal is my favourite novelist.
The psychologist's eye, the firm grasp of facts,
The honest atheism – unheard of in France.
Perhaps he's the one writer I envy?
And he made the best atheistic joke:
"God's excuse is that He doesn't exist."

4

Heine is my favourite lyric poet.
The adorable chords of his music
Surpass, for me, the thunder and lightning,
The downpours and the drizzle, of the rest.
And he's perfected that divine malice
Without which perfection seems fraudulent.
Nor must I put it out I do not know
Heinrich Heine and I are co-equal first
In our mastery of the German lyric.
I was partial to Byron at 13,
Especially his *Manfred*. Yet I reserve
My greatest praise for William Shakespeare,
Not because of his poetry or plays,
But because he created the archetype
Of the Caesar, so crucial to my work.
He didn't guess, he embodied the type.
The mightiest visions of reality
Presuppose the mightiest powers to act.
This helped resolve my central dilemma:
The man who acts through whom the seer works,
The Roman Caesar with the soul of Christ.

5

The greatest personal happiness I knew
Was Richard Wagner. I have never loved
Anyone as much as I loved Wagner.
Our days together, walking near Tribschen,
Are sacred to me forever, sacrosanct,

As pure and blue as the skies of Switzerland
We crammed with passionate revelations
Of all the private emotions we had known
And all those we had yet to explore.
Walking by lakes, through fields, in the mountains,
Those were the days we tested happiness,
Knocking it with the tuning fork of pain
To find out the depth of our ecstasy.
Passionate, witty, crass, mystical, sane,
The first time I saw him, I gasped out loud
(Out of earshot) struck dumb to see a man
Embody the spirit of uniqueness.
Nothing will ever diminish my shock.
What I saw, walking about so freely
Among men, I instinctively revered.
Though flesh and blood, he was to me born outside
The squalid incarnation of The Reich.
I'd found love, or tangible happiness.
I saw, too, what it meant to be a man,
And how uniquely placed he was to foil
All the rottenness he saw around him.
He was thirty-one years older than me.

6

I was a child of the 1840s,
And necessarily pessimistic
About the very concept of 'Germany'.
Was there anything to be thought at all,
Except revolutionary thoughts,
In a corrupt, corrupting state of things,
Where the bigot always came out on top?
Whether in scarlet toga or white pips
Was a matter of complete indifference...
All right! So Wagner was a revolutionary!
In 1849 he threw himself
Wholeheartedly into revolution

Which collapsed. He escaped to Switzerland
Shortly after his 36th birthday,
Living in exile for a dozen years.
During this time, he met his first bright fan,
Charles Baudelaire. And he first recognized
Delacroix. But Baudelaire was decadent,
The archetypal decadant, in whom
An entire species of artist mirrored
And buried itself.
So what did Wagner do
For which I could never forgive him?
That great man, on rebecoming German,
To put an end to his years in exile,
Condescended to the German people.
I could have forgiven him anything,
But *condescension*? Never! It cheapened him.
As far as Germany extends, it ruins culture.

7

To relieve social claustrophobia,
Smoke hashish. I could never have made it through
The insufferable corridor of my youth
Without the music of Richard Wagner.
Put it like that: Wagner was my hashish.
When I heard the piano score to *Tristan*,
I knew, from that moment on, I was hooked.
His earliest works didn't affect me,
Too commonplace, too dull, but even now
I hunger and thirst for a work of art
With the soft, scintillating infinity,
The sweet, dangerous felicity
Of *Tristan and Isolde*, but in vain.
The Meistersinger, The Ring, these are climb-downs.
For only those who have been sick enough
Can understand the voluptuousness
Of the great Richard Wagner at his best.

I think I know as well as anyone
How much he achieved. And I am proud to think
Our names will be linked together forever.

8

Out of my pantheon of household Gods,
I've mentioned food, drink, place, climate, leisure.
These have one thing in common: survival.
The active principle of this instinct
Filters the never-ending stimuli
Hitting the mind: this thought, not that, this smell,
This person to love, not that, and so forth.
The instinct to survive is why I am
The person I am and not someone else.
This alone makes identity unique.
Every time we pay the price to survive
We add to the burden of an unpaid debt.
To cope, we try to strike the right balance:
Self-preservation countered by wisdom.
The effort of maintaining this balance
Saps the strength of even the greatest minds...
The instinct to survive is best revealed
In retreat from normal circumstances.
Home, family, friends, neighbours, the office,
Inhibit freedom, initiative, the self.
It is perfectly natural to hate
The rôles foisted on us by other people
Coërcing us to their own ways of life.
No wonder a small voice whispers to us,
'Survive. Only survive.' Some don't listen.

9

I'll tell the parable of the scholar.
'Once upon a time, there was a scholar.
He bought a new trolley to wheel his books
Between the library and his study,

About two hundred or so every week.
With lavish diligence he stripped each book
Down to its bare secrets on his wanton desk.
He noted, copied, filed, till the day came
He indexed his files, and then his indices.
One day, much to his surprise, he noticed
He had stopped thinking. He had stopped having
Original thoughts himself. He could think,
But nothing except the thoughts of others.
He consoled himself with pungent critiques
On the creativity of others.
Time passed. He agreed, and he disagreed,
With what had already been thought and done,
Till the day came when he couldn't recall
What he'd wanted to do in the first place
Or why. His creative powers had dried up.
Under the dust, files, books, and bric-à-brac
His survival instinct had ossified.
He'd become a professional stuffed owl.
Settling for the worst, he seemed resigned
To a premature death, with nothing achieved.
I know. He was my friend.
Gifted, rich, and free, but dead at twenty-nine.'
Early in the morning on a hillside,
In all the tender and dawn of being,
To study a book? I call that *vicious*.

10

What comes after the art of survival?
As we taste the world, how do we become
What we are? (My most fiendish paradox.)
To realise ourselves, presupposes
We do not know who we are. To set up
Ideals like 'Know yourself' 'Love your neighbour'
Between the clear surface of consciousness
And thought, is like erecting a stone wall

Of language, between oneself and oneself,
Botched up from the ruins of history,
To help defeat the intention in hand!
   We must guard ourselves against grand language.
Sparkling words speckle the surface of thought:
The organising principle of mind,
Determined to grow in a unique brain,
Ponders the fact of brain, as brain mind.
   Mind is the nucleus pregnant in the cell,
Sinking at length, till fusing in the depths.
Slowly it grows, a mental embryo,
Uncoiling from sacs and yolky stretchings,
Side-tracks, wrong-turnings, and bold flourishes,
To fins of reason, flapping in the deep.
Like unilluminated mind at large,
It navigates the circuits of the cell
Towards the light of an adult purpose.
Slaked by the water which sustains it, mind
Soars through the silver surface like a fish,
A translucency of thought in the bright sun,
Celebrating the miracle of life.
   Nothing is coërced. Nothing is defined.
There is – a multiplicity of fact,
The very, and opposite of, chaos.
Thoughts known to be opposed to each other
Balance in harmony within the mind.
Eye and ear marry distance and measure.
Hierarchies of flesh rank themselves out.
The organising principle of mind
Causes the order of just uniqueness.

11

Until I saw the miracle of growth,
I never understood how I became.
I never wanted to be somebody.
I never encouraged sly ambition.

The surface of my mind was always clear
Out of which my life and my works appeared.
   I never wanted to improve on life.
I never wanted to be someone else.
I never wanted honours, money, sex,
(If I relished each passing temptation.)
I wanted to be what life wanted me to be.
   I never dreamed I'd be a Professor
At 24, although the fact that I had
The Chair of Classical Philology
At Basle University was plain to all.
   So how did I become me? By letting
It happen? No! By plucking out the roots
Of all the frauds and imposters of being,
False physiology, and bad conscience.

12

If asked what significance I attach,
If any, to my household pantheon,
My answer is that such trivial matters
Have always been more important to me
Than questions about God, eternal life,
Truth, virtue, sin, the soul, or the beyond.
People detect eternal verities,
Even the divinity of mankind,
In such solemn and vacuous conceits.
   Insight is a consequence of trapping
A fact in its natural habitat,
Ignoring brilliant satellite points
Containing nothing more concrete than thought.
Questions about morals, for example,
Or sin, have never given me trouble.
These are conceptions, not realities.
I wouldn't disown one of my actions
Simply because someone called it evil.
When a consequence *is* evil, the truth

Is all too easy to want to disown.
Yet how can I disown my own actions
If I myself am their own chief witness?
Disowning that is to betray conscience.
  I have never believed in morals or sin.
They have no place in my experience
Of reason. I distrust emotive words,
But not my intellectual conscience.
I am too nosey, too inquisitive,
To be satisfied by the crude answers
Masquerading as God's morality.
Ideas of God, as they came down to me,
Were quaint curiosities, bric-à-brac,
Dusted down by theological friends.
At best, such ideas are indelicate;
At worst, they are nothing more than 'Don't think.'
  Questions like 'The responsibility
Of government towards education',
So it might serve society justly,
Are sunk and muddied at the fountainhead
By such empty philosophers' conceits,
All of whom hold 'trivia' in contempt.
  It is, nonetheless, the proper function
Of the conscientious philosopher
To take, in all intellectual conscience,
Responsibility for the future.
He carries the teaching of the people
In his mind, as surely as he carries
The aegis of knowledge on his shoulders.
  Society is the image of thought.
No one assumes a heavier burden
Than the conscientious philosopher.
In a corrupt society, therefore,
The philosopher suffers the outrage
Of seeing the asinine in charge of thought.
  His stifled intellectual conscience

Must witness the fraudulent masquerade
Of polymorphous, pious theologians
Pompously invoking pie in the sky,
While all around them, chanting at their palms,
Men in poses, caught in eternal flux,
Sacrifice themselves to his usurpers,
Gored to the core by ideology.
  I see his mind's usurpers like failures
Taking out revenge on life, secretly
Converting the mass to their wounded wills.
  I want to be the opposite of this.
I want to be light, cheerful, uncluttered,
Praising the superabundance of life.
I don't want to be morbid or gloomy,
I don't want to be zealous or pious.
I want to make myself comprehensible
To the worst equally as to the best.
  To learn wisdom, I look at things as they are,
Without wanting to change or distort them:
Neither the past, the present, nor the future;
Neither the good, the bad, nor the evil.
  I will never 'endure' necessity.
And much less so the dishonest reporters
Idealists are, confronting cruelty.
I suffer the necessity, and love.

The Dream of Intelligence:3

Some creators are born posthumously,
And I am one of them. I may have hoped
I would be understood in my lifetime,
But I didn't want to be understood
If this meant being more misunderstood.
Nor did I misunderstand my own mind.
  Although it's my instinct to be modest,
I'm incapable of false modesty
If this obstructs what I'm trying to say.
I see it as one of life's rarest pleasures
To handle, open, and read my best books.
When no-nonsense Doctor Heinrich von Stein
Announced he couldn't understand a word
Of *Zarathustra*, I knew what he meant.
If he had understood six sentences,
He would have transcended the modern age
And found himself on The Rock of Ages.
  What I have to say trumps Schopenhauer.
What he said, he willed. I willed not to will.
Not that I want to underestimate
How much the innocent have delighted me
In the critical rejection of my books.
Only last summer, when my books upset,
Perhaps, the balance of German letters,
One fine Professor, teaching in Berlin,
Suggested I might try another form:
'Nobody takes any notice of verse.'
  Yet it was Switzerland, not Germany,
Which dropped two literary bombs on me.
Doctor J. Widmann, in the *Berner Bund*,
September the 16th 1888,

Writing about *Beyond Good and Evil*,
Emphasized his respect for the courage
Shown to abolish all decent feelings!
While Carl Spitteler, also in the *Bund*,
Categorized *Thus Spoke Zarathustra*
'An advanced exercise in style; though later,
Perhaps, he'd like to provide some content?'!
   Well, nobody can divine from a thing
Or book a meaning which is beyond him.
So if, as with me, I'm designating
Experience beyond the moral round,
Who will hear, what will be heard, when the first
News of such experience is published?
Nothing but an acoustic illusion
Gores at the ears of the outraged reader.
   My originality obscures me
Just as much as my life's experience.
Even those who might have understood me
Feel tempted to find fault with my meaning,
Not uncommonly saying the opposite
Of something I have stated in writing.
'Nihilism', perhaps, or 'cruelty',
Or 'a violent hatred of mankind',
Type-casting me as a new archetype
Encouraging delight in suffering
As the necessary price of progress.
   Whereas, in reality, what I've said
Is, in all particulars, the same as
The point of view of the tragic poet.
I teach it is the art of poetry
Which shows us best how to face suffering
Passionately, so that, reflected back
In the formal shapes of words, we see our pain
But naked and transfigured, being words,
To give us understanding which delights
Because every nuance of the pain is there.

Over and over we re-read the words
Astonished a poet has got it right.
  Can such psychology be popular?
Isn't it more probable our delight
Will get distorted in the daily press?
  My typology of men, for instance,
Has, almost universally, been seen
As something other than what I made it.
For into this typology I placed
One more type, whom I called the *uberman*,
The fruitful, as in 'uberous woman
Abounding in thought and milk for her child'.
[From the Old Teutonic form, 'übermensch',
Later resurrected in Goethe's *Faust*.]
  Everywhere, the *uberman*, the fruitful,
Is a type ineluctably thought of
As 'the superman' or 'the overman',
Connotating superiority,
Which is, God knows, the very opposite
Of how a provider feels for its kind.
  With perfect innocence, the fruitful type
Has, almost without a qualm, been thought of
As the ideal type, the higher species,
Half genius, half saint, half god, the point
And tip of subjective phantasy.
Whereas what I meant was *the provident*
Irrespective of moral attitude.
  The scholarly herd even accused me
Of falling foul of Darwin's Family Tree,
Installing my type as far above man
As Darwin places man above the apes!
Even of unconscious mendacity,
Like Thomas Carlyle's cult of the hero.
  Those to whom I suggested they should look
More to Caesar Borgia than to Parsifal,
To see this type, could hardly believe their ears.

Nor could I, I can tell you, when I read
A review of *Beyond Good and Evil*
In the Prussian *Nationzeitung:*
This saw my work as 'a sign of the times
Crystallizing the pure, the genuine
Junker philosophy of The Far Right,
Which even its own newspapers daren't print...'!
So I am not mindlessly incurious
About reviews of my books, good or bad.

2

That was said for the ears of Germany.
I do, however, have other readers,
Including people of intelligence,
Scholarship, rank, and even genius,
Whether in Paris, Stockholm, or New York,
Rome, Copenhagen, or Saint Petersburg.
I have been discovered haphazardly
But not in the flatlands of Germany.
In view of all this, I must emphasize
It is those who have never heard of me
Nor concerned themselves with philosophy
Who have given me the greatest pleasure.
As I say, my sincerest compliments
Come from the woman in the marketplace
Who hands me her sweetest bunches of grapes
Whenever she sees me approach her stall.
That's how far you've got to go to succeed.

3

I just don't have it in me to be grave.
To think German, to feel German, I could
Do anything, but this is beyond me.
My teacher, Professor Ritschl, maintained
Even my philological essays
Were rapturously imagined. To quote

Hippolyte Taine, people astonish themselves
Observing 'toutes mes audaces et finesses'.
   There is in me, even in the high form
Of the Greek dithyramb, a pinch of salt.
Ich kann nicht anders. Mirr Gött helpfen. (Amen).
To get the better of me calls for force,
Especially the force of delicacy.
The slightest hint of a frivolous mind
Kills me dead; and even, till they recant,
Disbars the mighty from the reckoning.
So do indigestion and jaded nerves.
The sine qua non is an iron stomach.
   Nor is it merely poverty of spirit
And its foul-smelling ancestor, self-love,
Which prohibit a man's understanding.
It's cowardice, hatred, a dirty mind,
Habitual resentment in the guts,
And that top-heavy inflationary
Belief in Mystical Establishments
No more with us than the man in the moon.
   The fact of the matter is, my best work,
Eerily nosing out a man's weakness,
Vomits *Disgust With Life* back in his face.

4

Four classes of people bring home to me
The various reactions to my work.
The first want nothing to do with content.
They're my friends. 'What could we say anyway?
We congratulate you on the progress
You've made in your new cheeriness of tone.'
Then there are the beautiful souls, the haughty
Preposterously mendacious people,
Who don't know what to do with me at all
But end up implying I'm beneath them.
'We happen to think you're not important.'

Dozy oxen, thirdly, feel their colleagues
(German, I add) cannot always agree
With what I say, 'though yes, they sometimes do.'
(I even heard this for *Zarathustra*!)
The fourth shelter in tight, sexualist cliques
Ostentatiously ignoring the world.
   There must be the habit of being stark,
Cheerfully face to face with cruel facts.
The ideal reader I imagine is
Cunning, cautious, courageous, charming, warm,
A born explorer, who will discover
For himself what plodders later achieve,
Who will, from habit, live dangerously.

5

I see my influence as a writer
May run to ruining a person's taste.
After me, most writers seem insipid,
Especially the philosophical ones,
And the blinkered, nihilistic poets.
There's always something clay-footed about
The anxieties of the second-rate.
   With me, anyone close enough in purpose
May recover the ecstasies of learning
Both within himself and in history.
I come from the heights, with my fingers burning,
Eyes too, and a mind stuffed with libraries.
Discounted by the birds, of course, laughed at.
But hanging fire over the great abyss...
   I've been informed I'm 'unputdownable',
Not that I believe that. There's too much there.
They say reading me ruins a night's sleep,
Which I do believe, recalling my theme
Is the transubstantiation of pain.

6

A time to speak about art, about style.
To communicate a state of pathos,
Using the letters of the alphabet,
Using the syllables of those letters,
Using words, and the rhythms of those words,
Using form, incorporating metre,
Using syntax and premeditation:
These are the intentions of any style.
  Because of the number of states there are,
Because of the number of parts to move,
There are any number of styles in art,
And therefore the perfect style for each art.
  Any style is justified, if it works.
A coiled steel spring, revolving smaller wheels
Counter-revolving larger wheels, whose hands
Dial a face, by which *the time* is read...
A gaunt committee, haggling through the night
(A window burning above the silenced streets)
Raising its hands, by which *our fate* is read...
An inky printer, thumbing out his type,
Slotting each letter squarely in the frame,
Mirror-imaging in inverted lead
Printed books, by which *poetry* is read...
Instinct is infallible about style:
'Good style' means nothing by itself, gestures
Empty of concrete rhetorical force.
  Effective style in art presupposes
There actually are people out there
Decoding the messages of pathos.
To whom, therefore, reading them, there must be
The imperative to communicate.
  The art of rolling rhythm, rolling on
Clause on phrase, overrolling phrase on clause,
Clause on phrase, till with momentum rising,
We rise and fall, and rising, rise and fall,

Fall and rise, falling and rising, rising
And falling, rising falling, and falling
Rising, happy to rise and fall, till full,
Passionate, and sublime, we come to rest:
I call this style the dithyrambic art,
After the Greek choric hymns sung in praise,
Intoxicating, vehement, and wild,
Of Dionysus, God of love and wine.
With it, I soared a thousand miles beyond
The world of contemporary poetry.

7

'His work forms a unique psychology'
Is, perhaps, the first thought of a reader
Who reads me like philologists read Horace
Scrutinizing the linguistic logic.
Universal propositions agreed
By homespun philosopher-moralists
Disintegrate there, like naïve blunders.
Take the belief that egotistical/
Non-egotistical are opposites,
When the ego itself is an ideal,
A loftly swindle! My work sees neither
The ego nor non-ego in our acts,
But unadulterated behaviour
Psychologically absurd to class
By looking at it outside inside out.
Take the words 'Man searches for happiness',
'Happiness is the reward of virtue':
That Circe of the brain, morality,
Seduces the logic of the virile
Out of all foundation, till (drugged) they think
Like nodding hogs, happiness is *selfless*.
To love, get a grip, be brave, down to earth.
Without brio, let's face it, life's a dead duck.
Women know this. They don't give a monkey's

About manhood's 'selfless objectivity'.
Dare I say what they want? That I know them
From Dionysian experience?
  Well? Perhaps I am the first psychologist
To understand the female archetype?
Yet I forbear being torn to pieces,
And the female archetype tears to pieces
Whatever she loves. I know these ladies.
Look, how stealthy, how they move, how they slip
Surreptitiously under the belly
Of the night, seeking out revenge on life.
Ah, what dangerous predators they are!
  Because women are cleverer than men,
They are, in this proportion, more evil.
They recognize 'virtue' as decadence.
The beautiful ones, to continue this,
Are physiologically askew:
They seek out the shapes they do not possess,
Rejoicing in the conquest of 'the good'.
'The good, virtuous man', who obstructs her,
Is soon swept aside with a fine sweep of skirt!
  Their fight for 'equal rights' is a symptom
Every doctor knows of political disease.
A woman, the more she is a woman,
Resists 'rights in general', since she knows
The balance of nature, engineering
The eternal war between the sexes,
Predisposes her the majority.
But 'rights in particular'? All out war!
  Let me give my definition of love,
The only one worthy of philosophy.
The beginning and the end of love,
And the motive by which it keeps going,
Is eternal war between the sexes.
So how does a man 'redeem' a woman?
By getting her a child... Women need children...

A man is only the means to the end.
  Watch out, though, for the emancipated,
Who, incapable of bearing children,
Turn their hatred against normal mothers.
The emancipated are the outlaws
In the world of the female archetype,
The beaten, whose first instinct is revenge.
Their war against men is a mere pretext.
By elevating themselves as ideals,
They aim to lower the rank of the rest.
And what better means of achieving this
Than trousers, a touch of learning, plus the
Political voting rights of cattle?
  Let me emphasize to death the high law
I uphold against sexual bigots,
Whose political attitude to sex,
(Through the impure hint of impurity
Stridently preaching in public places),
Poisons good conscience in sexual love
To incite violation of nature:
This is the deadliest crime against life,
The deadly sin against the holy ghost.

8

Who controls the genius of the heart?
Who is the tempter, the born pied-piper
Of conscience? Whose is the hidden face?
Who controls the genius of the heart?
Whose voice descends to the soft underbelly
Of the working day? Who winks and looks looks
And never without a hint of enticement?
Who's mastered the art of appearances
Constraining an audience to observe
The more closely, to draw it further in?
Who controls the genius of the heart?
Who teaches the loud and self-satisfied

The art of listening? Who smooths rough souls,
Arousing in them taste for sweet desire,
To rest, still as memory, the deep sky
Holding the mirror of itself in them?
Who controls the genius of the heart?
Who transforms the greedy and clumsy hand
To a jolt of divinity in air
Divining the hidden water, whose drops
Of clear, silver intelligence suffuse
The opaque earth? Who's the divining-rod
To each wet grain of cold gold undisturbed
Embedded in the banks of mud and muck?
Who controls the genius of the heart?
From whose touch, richer, do we walk away,
Dazed or graced, part shocked, but not indebted,
Wiser, more ourselves, better, deeper, truer
Than we were, blown open, fanned by the air
Walking alone in a temperate zone?
Who controls the genius of the heart?
Walking, tender perhaps, perhaps fragile,
Brooding new power, thoughtful, hopeful, we're
Stung by the gist of some malicious joke
To laugh at ourselves, abounding with life.
Who controls the genius of the heart?
I call the faculty Dionysus,
The reason-melting power of the heart.

The Dream of Intelligence:4

My life-story is a reconstruction
Of the background and writing of my books.
I wrote my life into them, and in them
I live once more how I became myself.
I pursue my own thread through my own maze,
And out again, to make sense of my life.
   To reconstruct *The Birth of Tragedy*,
First published in 1872,
I must first admit it had an effect
Strictly because of what was wrong with it.
This was the implication Wagnerism
Was able, in theory and practice,
To ignite the visionary furnace.
One result of this was that Wagner,
From that time on, aroused a profound hope.
Sixteen years later, some people still think
(Even in the context of *Parsifal*!)
I am personally responsible
For the high ideals they hold of Wagner.
What's worse, they like to call it 'The *Re*birth
Of Tragedy', as if my book were nothing
But Wagner's mythopoeic point of view.
   The living core and model of my book
Was ignored. 'Hellenism and Pessimism,
Or How the Greeks Overcame Pessimism'
Would have been a more accurate title.
The tragedies of the Greeks are the proof
They were not pessimistic. Schopenhauer
Got this, as he got so many things, wrong.
   Rereading it now, in a neutral light,
I am sure the work belongs earlier.

Who would suppose it was begun so late,
In earshot of cannon fulminating
At the battle of Wörth? Or puzzled out
On cold September nights by an Orderly
In the Medical Corps, going his rounds,
Working the tents below the walls of Metz
In the Franco-Prussian War, 1870?
I see it belongs fifty years before
To Hegel's heyday in the 1820s.
Perhaps it would be wise to admit
It even smells offensively Hegelian?
Its broad disinterest in politics
Assures it a non-German dimension,
Though Schopenhauer's cadaverous perfume
Lingers to a few sultry propositions.

2

I took the great Hegelian idea
Of dialectical opposition
Of fundamental forces (including
The ones which make us as we are, and those
Making the natural world as it is)
And stripped it down to what it's worth to me:
Thesis, antithesis, synthesis:
The thesis of the Dionysian,
The Apollonian antithesis,
And that rare miracle of synthesis,
The psychology of the tragic poet.
To originate my moral ethics.
In this world, the agony of forces
Generates visionary poetry,
As in the Greek mind, the opposition,
Dionysian/Apollonian,
Evolved the drama (the resolution
Of opposites being the finished play.)
Both show our capacity to rejoice

Contemplating agony of spirit
Transformed to beauty in a work of art.
  Caught in this Hegelian perspective,
People, never before set face to face
With the paradox of their own delight
In their own most horrific suffering,
Suddenly understood my point of view.
The incomprehensible succumbed. Pain,
Unique in the particular fact of each
Individual and private sorrow,
Which had before baffled understanding,
Rose from the depths of the unconscious mind
To redeem us in our innocence,
Wonderstruck before the mirror of art.

3

The two crucial advances in the book
Were, first, the psychological insight
Into the Dionysian force
Both in nature and in our own minds.
This, uninhibited instinct, when checked
And held by the Apollonian force,
Made, root, trunk and branch, art's flowering tree.
And second, a thing made new: Socratism.
Socrates was for the first time unmasked
As a force in Greek degeneration.
He was not the summit of Greek thought at all.
In short, I saw he was a decadent,
Whose rationality against instinct,
Whose rationality at any cost,
Was a dangerous, irrational force
Threatening to undermine the tragic,
Irreproachable attitude to life.
  I maintained a profound, hostile silence
To Christianity throughout the book.
But I honoured the two Greek Gods, because,

Though clearly contradictory forces,
They did not negate aesthetic values,
The only values the book recognized.
I took careful note how Christianity
And Nihilism, in theory opposed,
Exchanged bottomless rapport objecting
To the clear vision of reality
Revealed by the poets' tragic viewpoint.
Whereas my Hegelian perpective
Constrained to define its affirmation.

4

This beginning was remarkably odd.
I had discovered a classic pretext
In Ancient Greece for my own agony.
I knew I was someone who was suffering
The Dionysian phenomenon;
By, at the same time, typing Socrates
A decadent, I was able to see
Why I was so little preconditioned
To moral reflex. I saw that morals
Were characteristically Socratic:
Reasons to oppose to the instincts of life.
I couldn't have that. My explanation,
To account for my own experience,
Had to go deeper than conscious reason.
I saw how the answer lay in tragedy,
Which worked at a deeper level of the mind.
I saw how the suffering I was caused
Had nothing to do with morals, but life.
Moralising about it was foolish.
As a result, I was able to see,
Pace Socrates, that morality
Is the all-too-typical precursor
Of decadence. Therefore, that I could make
A breach in the history of knowledge.

5

It was time for the dawn of a new age
In which man's moral orientation
Was secured not from rational logic
But the psychology of tragedy.
  How high above the slight, tiny clatter
Of optimism tilting with pessimism
I flew on the wings of these two insights!
A mere, passing prelude to the true war:
Degenerate instinct turned against life
With the full ferocity of revenge.
  Buddhism, Christianity, Nihilism,
The philosophy of Schopenhauer,
All the ideals of every complexion:
These were the types of avenger I saw.
  Set against them stood *Miraculous Fire*,
The forge and fertile source of all things.
Molten, unimpressed, mercurial, pure,
It roared in the furnace, Eternal Mind.
And while the rest negated, it affirmed.
There was no material unaffirmed
Either in nature or the human brain.
Shame, guilt, pain, torture, murder: all affirmed.
The avengers, too, scheming: all affirmed.
The guns, the bombs, the poisons: all affirmed.
There was no material unaffirmed.
It had the sound of one syllable, Y E S,
Hissing agreement through the toads of war.
Nothing disturbed it. It stood unimpressed,
Its great aortas pumping white-hot rock.
This was the force round which the sacred moves
As stars around the night or people God,
Hell-tortured God, damned beauty crying death,
In moving, motionless, its fiery eye
Penetrating to the core of vengeance.
  This Yes to life symbolizes insight

Achieved by the techniques of the poets
Working outside the door of the furnace.
  To understand how requires courage,
And courage strength, for these two exactly
Together measure the approach to *Fire*.
Those who miss the point never fathom it.
Decadence loves the lie. And those to whom
Decadence winks, soon fall in love with lies.
Decadence abhors *Fire*, presupposing
What it most abjures will never happen.
It courts the luxurious, gilding alive
The living images of its desire.
  When I perceived the Dionysian
Just as much in The-Earth-In-Cataclysm
As my own heart, and both were tumbling *Fire*
Unconscious of the issue of my fate,
I stopped and stood above my sunlit desk,
Alert as a bird in a burning tree,
Sensing Dionysian energy
Thundering the wooden pews of makeshift eternity.
I saw no need to refute Schopenhauer,
Christianity, nor Plato himself.
I smelt *putrefying moralities*.

6

How through the poets I learnt to master
The visionary furnace, opening
And closing the door, I spelt out over
The next sixteen years. The point, however,
I wish to extract here, belongs to this
Key phase of my autobiography,
Not at the end of *Twilight of the Idols*
Where I published it in 1888.
  It is only in the psychology
Of the Dionysian Mysteries,
Sacrosanct to the God's Temple precincts,

That the noblest fact of the Greek instinct,
Which kept it from depressive pessimism,
Made itself abundantly obvious.
  So how did the Temples work exactly?
How did the weird Mysteries operate?
The event celebrated was simple:
Procreation through sexuality.
The human sexual experience
Was re-enacted (with due reverence
And full ceremonial rites) to stage
A scale model of life indoors, in which
The pains of childbirth symbolized all pain.
  Sexual attraction; shyness; courtship;
The sense of exaltation; of wonder
Touching a cosmos of beautiful form;
The inexhaustible rapture of sex;
Erotic, ecstatic impregnation:
Everything that guaranteed the future,
And therefore the pain, of life, was acted.
  The importance of the ceremony
Lay in the audience's overview,
That, just as the sense of divinity
Bestowed in extenso on two people
Was set in strict, logical proportion
To the pains and the dangers of childbirth,
So the pains and dangers were known,
But set in ratio to the greater
And rarer miracle of life itself.
  This was the Dionysian message.
The wonders of sex, pregnancy, and birth
Were seen in the same relation to pain,
As the seamless live continuum of pain
And the shattering violence of life
Were seen in relation to the cosmos.
  The Dionysian initiate
Understood all pain like a mountain range

He scaled alone towards the adult peaks;
Clinging to cliffs; crawling the endless rock;
Snowed out of sense; scalpelled alive by knives
Whistling out of winds swallowing the mountain;
Living or dying; and if surviving
Tramping the white torture to the snowline
Above the high green upland of pasture
Dazzling now on the far side of pain:
Below, the floating hills, the fertile valleys,
Fretted with flowers Greece redeems each spring,
Of philosophical understanding.

7

Medusa was another name for this,
The drama of confrontation with pain.
Acting on stage in the Temple precincts,
A young tragic poet tells the story:
'In the Libyan desert where she lay
Medua slept with ah, the perfect form.
Her famous hair was snakes, which writhed and hissed,
Coiling on the stones which were her pillows.
But all the rest, to my red-blooded eye,
Was, outstretched, naked, lying on her back,
Careless and dreaming of being taken,
Woman, woman, woman, woman, woman.
'I smiled because that fatal loveliness,
That shape to end all shapes, would kill a man,
If he so much as looked at it alive.
But in my art and in my fine upstanding,
Seeing her reflected in my shield
This poetry is, I updrew my sword,
This pen which wrote the deed of violence,
And struck her with a blow which chopped her head
Clean off her perfect form, and killed her dead.
'Her head I then speared into this wallet,
Sacred to Hermes and the Stygian Nymphs,

I carried for the purpose; and shut; because
Even now, despite decapitation,
It turns to stone whoever might behold it.
  'Around, about, and in the desert, leaned
Valiant warriors before my time:
Scholars, farmers, craftsmen, soldiers, poets,
Heroic hope had lured to this end,
To butcher the Medusa and win fame.
With arm aloft, or crawling through the sand,
Each contending hero, still advancing,
Immortalised Romantic courage doomed.
  'Around, about, and in the desert, leaned
Valiant warriors before my time
Littering the sands, petrified, relics,
A gaunt museum of the Gorgon, pain.'

8

The love for, and the affirmation of, life,
I saw as the greatest gift of the Greeks.
I saw their veneration was holy.
Life was affirmed, even though men died
Inexhaustibly, torturing credence,
And all manner of battledress and boots
Trampled the buried eye that's not yet born.
Life was affirmed, even in the knowledge
Of aboriginal calamity,
Cannibalism, human sacrifice,
Holocaust, premeditated genocide,
And that absolute pursuit of evil
For the creative genius found there,
Resentment, and not some counterfeit,
Thinking and capable of even worse.
  Sexuality was venerated
As the one known tangible source of life,
A way out, so to speak, for a lost soul
Circumnavigating a world of pain,

Tormented by the maplessness of death.

9

There was no question of ousting pity
From its established status in the mind,
Simply of not letting it dominate it.
Nor any question of backing actions
Which gave tacit endorsement to terror.
There was, in fact, never any attempt
By poets 'to correct, refine, or purge'
Divine, human, or bestial emotions
In a classic work of art, 'catharsis'
As Aristotle misunderstood it.
The technique of the poets was simpler:
To present reality as it is.
Revelations of pity and terror
Tore at the poets' chordae tendonae,
But they never let that influence them.
They venerated, because they loved, life.
This sole fact explains how they both suffered
Mortality and made immortal works.

10

Before I saw the Dionysian
Transfigure philosophical pathos,
Where was the wisdom of tragedy? Lost.
For two hundred years before Socrates,
Among the giants of Greek philosophy,
I searched for it in vain, or found little.
I retain a doubt about Heraclitus,
Sensing more in him than anyone else.
In practice, of course, it is typical
Of philosophy, throughout its history,
That such respect for beauty *and* horror,
Such love for creation *and* destruction,
Such veneration, *because of love*, for life,

Is the one thing philosophy abhors.
  It is this very point, nevertheless,
Which is the vital distinguishing mark
Of Dionysian philosophy:
This love, which foresees pain and violence,
Yet still concurs with life; this love, which looks
Profoundly into horror as it is,
And joy, to redeem them as they are;
This love is *the wisdom of tragedy*
The God Apollo called Dionysian.
  It remains true, nonetheless, that this view,
Despite inferences in Heinrich Heine,
Goethe, and Pythagorian philosophy,
Is essentially my own discovery.
What I call 'the eternal recurrence',
The everlasting force inside the wisdom,
Just might have been taught by Heraclitus.
At least the Stoa, that great hall in Athens
Colonaded, entablatured, and adorned
With frescoes of the battle of Marathon,
Where Zeno lectured Stoic disciples,
Inherited almost all its ideas,
Or the better part, from Heraclitus,
And shows tantalising traces of it.

11

A tremendous hope spoke out of this book.
Let us come back a hundred years from now,
To Germany in 1989.
Let ideology dominate man,
But let corruption be found not absolute.
I promise a new age of tragedy.
This hallowed technique, sanctifying life,
Will be reborn from the ashes of war.
  Then, that self-imposed discipline in life,
Which takes on the hardest tasks (like lifting

Humanity up by its own bootstraps)
Will, by insight into the decadence
Feeding on the very soul it governs,
Make Greek Dionysian pride once more
Possible on Earth. Out of which, men will,
Grappling with the never-lessening force
Of the flesh-fired furnace of affliction,
Dramatise the wisdom of tragedy.
  Men will again endure the ordinance
Of fratricidal, blood-embittered dawns;
Witness the schizophrenic crack zigzag
The white cloud of truth; stampede with the crowds
Chanting through the marble halls of power,
The sea at night pitching buoyant soldiers;
Pinch philosophers awake to mothers
Ripping the sky's throat to see their babies
Bayonetted to the earth they once had loved;
Flick the whip on donkeys dragging corpses,
Blazing bonfires roaring endless hills;
Torture conscience, the cruel lust to kill
Turning inwards, turning into guilt;
Reflect on bloodshed and the cause of war;
Grieve for parents gone; hang hope; spurn prayer
As the last refuge of the fatuous;
Syringe eternal youth in flowing veins
Draining down to oceanic despair
And permanent narcosis of the mind:
As life dissolves once more, and all on stage,
The amphitheatre of tragedy,
Sacred to the Dionysian God.

The Dream of Intelligence:5

How could Wagner have come to terms with this?
How could his acolytes have seen themselves
Settling into the high noon of drama
In which the *ubermen* of the spirit,
The poets of the art of tragedy,
Consecrate themselves to the love of man?
Could they have understood Greek redemption?
  The pathos of my divorce from Wagner
Was world-historic. I had come to see
For a work to be possessed by greatness
Two quite distinct things had to coincide:
Magnificence in the perpetrator
And magnificence in the spectator.
  Nothing, I saw, possessed greatness in itself.
The disappearance of constellations,
The destruction of civilizations,
The cataclysm of war yielding bloodshed
And loss of life on unheard of scales,
Perfect harmony in the Global State:
A mild spring in winter blows away
All of them, as if they were flakes of snow,
Unless grasped by the sufficient witness.
  Even the great act of a great man,
Like Wagner at the Bayreuth Festival
Realising his world myth in *The Ring*,
Dissolves like a dream, if there is no one,
No sufficient witness, to describe it.
  When a great act disturbs the clear surface
Of the still lake of human memory,
It must, in some sense, have misjudged the time
And the place to register on our minds,

If it is destined to flatten and fade
As a ripple of no significance.
The great act, and the great consequences
Of the great act, have always acknowledged
Greatness, and the recognition of greatness,
Belong together.
Wagner in Bayreuth,
The pettiness of German wretchedness,
These were the screens on which I projected
My knowledge of all-redemptive vision!
I even projected my mental traits
Onto Wagner and the Germans: the fine
Interweave of light and dark powers,
The will to power as never before,
The courage to create as never before,
The will to act besting the will to know.
The youthful folly of my projections
Turned on the purpose of Greek tragedy:
I needed a modern Alexander
To cut the Gordian knot of Europe.

2

My passion transfigured Wagner's music,
And not just his music, but the whole world,
Into the spirit I had within me.
My knowledge of the art of tragedy,
Projected with such proud wish-fulfilment
Onto this hero of my younger days,
Flattered Wagner's mythopoeic viewpoint;
Which did little more than transform the world
And himself into a mythology
Plundered from baroque medievalism.
Wagner himself may have suspected this.
The sense of history, of which my age,
The late 19th century, was so proud,
Was in fact, I saw, decadent, corrupt,

Another cryptic instance of decay,
The blind over-emphasis on the past.
  We need history to act, to live life
In the light of ancestral dignity;
But not too much of it, for this causes
Lassitude, weariness, angst, exhaustion,
The sense of an infinite weight crushing
All joy, all life, all spontaneity.
And yet it is the study of history,
Especially the Hellenic, which helps us
Overcome the study of history.
  Too many old ideas squander the new.
Greatness reacts to life instinctively.
With it, history is itself the teacher
Teaching us to mastermind history.
The love of life hates the superfluous.

3

We envy cattle munching in a field
Because they seem to have no sense of time.
A cow simply forgets time all the time,
A feat we are unable to manage.
Animals live unhistorically.
Every moment, every fall of a leaf,
Dies with the moment, and is forgotten.
With us, the moment, the fall of a leaf,
Returns like a ghost to haunt happiness.
When the first spring petal falls, we fall too.
The grazing deer, the children playing house,
The green lawns surrounding the white mansion,
Like the vision of a lost paradise,
Arouse the vile consciousness of envy.
We see life flower with no sense of time,
While we ourselves are dying of too much.
  The mildest happiness which survives time
Is better than happiness which passes.

This is, perhaps, why no philosophers
Seem better justified than the Cynics.
Aren't animals, who are Perfect Cynics,
Living proof of the truth of Cynicism?
   It is forever the same thing which makes
Happiness happiness. The sense of time
Dissolves. We feel unhistorically.
Without the power to dissolve the past,
To recreate ourselves out of the present,
We are ipso facto condemned to watch
The state of things coming into being.
We are condemned to watch reality
Made concrete in the stream of becoming.
We witness how one thing becomes itself,
Then, how everything becomes something else
Once more. And we can forget none of it.
Like the true pupils of Heraclitus,
We will, in the end, hardly dare to lift
A finger, petrified by the vision
Of becoming coming into being.
   By not using our power to command
The vision of reality to shut,
Action becomes impossible. We stand,
Like dumb witnesses in the dock of time,
In a state of permanent sleeplessness.

4

At what point exactly, in the steady
Unfolding of life in The Parent State,
Can we afford to ignore history?
When is it better to forget the past?
When does responsibility to life
Outweigh gratitude to the status quo?
When are we certain it's wiser to laugh,
To slap the table and stop worrying
About time, than conform to convention?

Strung out between two outlooks on the high wire,
The time-linked view of life and the time-free,
In which direction do we inch our way?
Do we live like the animals, or where
History breaks the individual?
For years, the true answer to this question
Eluded me. Suddenly I found it.
It is the plasticity of the mind,
Our ability to remake ourselves
Out of the experience of the past,
Rather than be demoralised by it,
Which is the mark of human survival.
I saw there is a universal law.
A living life is bounded by a line.
The strong and healthy individual
Always exists within a given space.
Of all the world, the greatest men, I saw,
Who do not possess plasticity enough
To bend with the necessity of change,
Crack under the pressure of history,
Leaking the ectoplasm of malcontent.
Whereas, bound by the supple hand of grace,
Health is comely, definite, and hard. It
Hammers home the nail with a good conscience.
I saw how surviving experience
Depends as much as not on forgetting.
Maintaining the balance is the key thing.
Too much forgetting makes us animals.
Too much historical sense makes us gods.
And the end of either way is horror.

5

Living in the thin air of the mountains,
The Unhistorical Man smokes his pipe:
'History is of little importance.
I feel neither temptation to belong

Nor take part. One day is enough. The aim
Of existence arrives with every moment.
Red squirrels leap through the silver birches.
A falling feather floats on the duckpond.
In my shack, a yellow trapezium
Dandles the flying buttress of the sun.
Radiance is the news. The nightingales,
Clamouring in the branches, give me peace.'
  Shouted in the city, the news looks bad.
Historical Man furrows his forehead.
'Happiness has set below the skyline,
And agitation is packing my bags.
The brief of the past compels the future.
Over the horizon, the same thought dawns.
Our lives have evolved to such a degree
Living them has become mechanical:
Tired animals migrating through our lives.'
  The Unhistorical Man chops a log,
Hobbling in with kindling for the grate.
'Wisdoms agree. Past and present are one.
Nature, animal, or man, the same forms
Come and go. If one or two become extinct,
What is that in a teeming universe?'
He lights the kindling from a hand-cupped sun,
'There is one value which does not alter.
The language of change is always the same.'
He ponders his words as he prods the brew,
'The fresh green letters are gathered outside time
And the holy word is cooked in the pot.'
  Holding forth at a Conference Centre,
Historical Man lectures his colleagues,
'It may be that, from a world point of view,
History is a western prejudice.
So be it. But don't knock it. We *are* western.
We would, of course, be the first to admit
Suprahistorical views are wiser,

If we add the gloss, 'but we've got more life'.
Even when copulating in the dark,
As lusty and mindless as animals.
We do, at least, procreate the future.'
  Unhistorical Man talks to the fire,
'Too much scientific knowledge obscures
The human impulse it is here to serve.
When history becomes a pure science,
Life is over, and we're settling accounts.
The ablest work done by historians
Gives a sensation of something happy.
Such an art can never be a science.
It is a doctor in war, dragging out
A bloody child alive from the wreckage.'

6

And so I began my meditation
On conflicting theories of history.
  In one of his essays, Schopenhauer says,
'Philosophy has the distinction
Of presupposing absolutely nothing
As known.' Isn't it inapposite, then,
To presuppose knowledge of history?
  I see, *The urge to shine in acts and works,*
To stand out like the great in history,
And so encourage others to greatness;
The urge to understand cultural roots,
To plumb the pantheons of self-knowledge,
And so help posterity help itself;
And the urge to find an answer to pain.

7

Men of power and action, who make it,
Need history most. Examples abound
In the fields of politics and warfare,
But poetry, too, is no exception.

Take Shakespeare and Goethe, for example.
Exhausting living models, they ransacked
The historical archives of their times
To stem the fever of their genius.
Masters of politics might burn less hot,
But even so, they are formidable.
Polybius the Greek, for example,
Who flourished in the second century
Before the birth of Christ, illuminates
The Rise of the Roman Empire. It's clear
How anyone who wants to school himself
To govern a state, bearing trouble well
By knowing worse, must read Polybius.
Men of power and action set their sights
On the prosperity of the nation,
The happiness of mankind as a whole,
And only incidentally themselves.
Never seduced by glittering prizes,
Except fame, because it's exemplary,
Their motive is nothing less than the hope
That that which makes man worthy of honour
Will last forever. To convince themselves,
They see, in the mind's eye, a mountain range
Uniting man across the centuries.
Monumental history has spurred them.
It is, unfortunately, this urge to shine
Which sparks off the worst international wars.
'The road to immortality,' they say,
'Runs through the tidy, bureaucratic, dull,
Stolid, shallow, stifling populations . . .',
Not yet disembarrassed of their contempt.
A battle of titanic force begins.

8

Fame is more than 'the tastiest morsel
Of our egotism' Schopenhauer called it.

It's our belief in solidarity
With the greatest achievements of the past,
A protest and a demonstration against
The passing away of generations
And the heart-breaking transience of love.
  A man destined for immortality
Finds 'threescore years and ten' a witty joke.
For him, there is nothing more than the moment
In which to give up his entire being
To life. *There is nothing left to bury,*
The dross is consigned to mortality.
To see that honour was once possible
Is to see it is possible again.
The Renaissance rose on a hundred men.
  Yet circumstance is never the same twice.
It is the abstract spirit of a thing,
And nothing else, which is repeated.
It is absurd, a joke, to imagine
History repeats itself verbatim.
'When the stars re-reach their once-held orbits,
Stoic re-plots with Epicurean
To murder Caesar. The clouds part so, so
Columbus re-discovers America . . . '
This is what happens when astrologers
Teach science. Astrology looks through
The glorious eyes of astronomy,
And, dazzled by the stars, concocts the future
Out of the sober look of the universe.
The connection between cause and effect,
As Hume revealed, cannot even be proved,
Let alone held responsible for that!

9

The danger of the monumental mind
Is susceptibility to hubris.
The brave are inspired to foolhardiness,

And the suffering to fanaticism.
In the worst possible instance, the man
Who mirrors the hubris of his people
Comes to power, sickening from the form
Known as *pseudologia phantastica*,
Psychopathic inferiority.
The ground is laid for the worst kind of war.
Hate of inferiority becomes
Destruction on a monumental scale,
Taking out revenge on life when quite mad.
  Something similar happens in the arts.
When, though proud, an artist is weakly endowed
With the grandeur of creativity,
Yet holds the critical field, he conspires
Against the strongest artists of his time,
Taking out revenge on his lack of talent.
Quoting the canon of art, he comments,
'None of the authority of the past.'
He blocks advancement, setting in the way
The masterworks of the past, consigning
The 'feeble efforts' of his rivals
To the margins of poverty and neglect.
As deadly as he's envious, he poisons
The innocent press, till the popular vote
Always finds against the strongest artists.
Art is employed to assassinate art.
'Let the dead bury the living,' we joke.

10

The urge to understand cultural roots,
To plumb the pantheons of self-knowledge,
And so help posterity help itself:
This is the antiquarian's motive.
  To him, antique objects seem invested
With a peculiar fascination.
The broken pots from a ruined city

Bring to life the daily grind of the streets.
He feels beyond himself. He steps outside
The sense of individual being
To recover the spirit of the tribe.
It was, in fact, the antiquarians
Who dug up the buried light of Italy
And woke the poets of the Renaissance
To the genius of the classic past.
  Antiquarians resurrect the past.
The noblest use of their tools and relics
Is the evocation of a people,
Whose descendants (even if living in
Abject poverty) take hope and courage,
Pride and satisfaction, through contact
With their forefathers in the great ages past.
  Hoeing thin earth on a grey mountainside,
There are those who live their lives in this way,
Within the compass of the antique law.
So to their ancient festivals all come
On summer nights, climbing the terraced hills,
The mountain roads, towards the village squares.
For there, on cooling stone, beneath the trees
Shading the tables in the fading heat,
The salt of the earth arrive, to pull up chairs,
To break their bread or cheese or pour their wine,
As violin and clarinet give way
To dazzling bouzoukis – the pigs-on-spits
Turning over charcoal in the cave-red night.
Here is the antidote to national angst
Wandering the world in search of money,
As men and women dance beneath the stars.
Their bark-hard faces venerate the young,
And praise awake the starlit mountain dawn.

11

The danger is, the antiquarian,

Dominated by the past, sees nothing
Except tradition worthy of respect.
Life is not so much revered as preserved.
  We sense the abuse of preservation
Turning into personal obsession.
We follow shyly through the polished halls
Appalled by a butterfly collection.
We tramp back from the flag-stoned wine cellar,
Denied a drink, to admire the bookshelves.
Trapped at last by our host, we sneeze, learning
Absolutely nothing whatsoever
While the dotty bellows blows the dust off
Bibliographical minutiae.

12

The critical historian attempts
To satisfy the third, more pressing need:
The urge to find an answer to pain.
  Won in the white of pure created light,
He builds, piece by piece, his dwelling-place,
His metaphysical house, stone by stone,
Beam by beam, hod by hod, tile by slow tile:
He is constructing a world history
He would like to have come from, but doesn't,
Out of one he does come from, but dislikes.
  He is trying to strike the right balance
Between the three types of historian.
Philosophy, for him, he's come to see,
Is the urge to find an answer to pain.
  His chief source of power is the Greek mind.
Throughout the epoch of their greatest strength,
The Greeks maintained an astonishing hold
On the unhistorical sense. They saw,
As though by divine inspiration, life,
'The upshot of history', is more than it.
Artistic expression erupted. Style

Blossomed in every attitude to life,
Whether in marble, dancing, or debate.
   They believed man the divine animal,
A summing-up I happen to share.
Now, by contrast, we're just the opposite,
The godless humans. How did this happen?
   Nothing is more important to me
Than the restoration of German thought:
To reunite the German mind once more
In the highest art, beyond politics,
The sine qua non of cultural style.
As the old dramatist, Grillparzer, said,
'We feel in abstractions'. And the most, I add,
Seductive of them all is history.

The Dream of Intelligence:6
[Nietzsche's Meditation on History]

We need history, not to predict life,
But to liberate ourselves from pain.
The critical vision points to one end:
Liberation from pain and affliction.
   The idea we can predict the future
On the basis of what has gone before
Ignores the strange asymmetry of time.
Copernicus may read Democritus,
Dante may study Thomas Aquinas,
But Aristotle cannot read Newton,
Nor Goethe Fyodor Dostoevsky.
Although we interpolate from the past
To construct our picture of the present,
To extend this to predict the future
Is to name a thinker who's not yet born,
And not only that but to read him too.
We can prove history is influenced
By developments in human knowledge;
We can also prove we cannot predict these;
Therefore we cannot predict history.
   I am myself the logical fulcrum
On which I pivot to understand time.
Criticism of history, in my case,
Is how I create an answer to pain,
And the bedrock of my philosophy.
   If history is the story of time
Misconstrued, which leads us into error,
The story of time must be told again.

2

The most truthful of the sciences,
The honest Naked Goddess, philosophy,
Turns, in time, into a soliloquiser,
A lame, grey Muse, hobbling home ignored.
No one lives philosophically now.
That unbreakable bond, with which the Greeks
Upheld themselves as Stoics, once they had
Ascertained loyalty to the Stoa,
Is unheard of in a pluralist culture
Where the Naked Goddess goes unheeded.
We may think, speak, write, lecture, or publish
Philosophy, but we may not live it.
We have become flesh-and-blood data banks
Inside the shaping cage of history.
We fool ourselves this is philosophy,
But the truth is we are trapped. History
Chickencoops the slave imagination.
Nor is it any loss of dignity
For us to admit personal failure
Face to face with the scale of this challenge.
Trapped in time's cage, we've become clever.
We think we're the equal of the Romans
Simply because we understand them.
As for the Greeks, we read their poetry
Nursing delusions we too feel like that.
We're all trapped in the same cage together.
Hollowed out by ingrown self-loathing,
Our immoderate hatred of the Muse
Betrays an essential lack of control
The Romans knew as *impotentia*.
If history is the story of time
Misconstrued, which leads us into error,
The story of time must be told again.

3

Our historical objectivity
Persuades us to think of ourselves as strong,
That is, just, juster than all other ages.
Yet Socrates said, 'To persuade ourselves
We possess virtue we do not in fact possess
Borders on madness.' Are we perhaps mad?
The truth is, the drive to, and the strength for,
Justice, deserves our highest admiration,
Just as it demands our fiercest defence.
If magnanimity is a virtue,
And the rarest of virtues is justice,
This is because they are human nature
In its most exhilarating form.
   Only in so far as the truthful man
Enshrines the first principle of justice
As the first principle of Government,
Can greatness derive from the drive for truth.
The drive for truth alone is not enough,
For truth grows in justice, not in itself.
This is why so few people work for truth,
A tree everywhere rooted in justice:
They don't like to test its grounds too closely.
   So where does the secret of justice lie?
Are we juster than previous ages?
The only fact we can be certain of
Is that justice grows from strength, not weakness.
Only strength dares to oppose the unjust:
Weakness bows his head, and tolerates shame.

*

   There is a whole school of historians
Who think they know how to be objective.
They are painters painting a stormy sea
Serenely convinced they're detached from it.

They insist, 'We paint only what is there.'
This is simple-minded superstition.
Or do they suppose that, by the evening,
The stormy sea, exactly as it is,
Sketches, drafts, designs, draws, and paints itself
On a white and impassive medium?
To think of history objectively
Is the silent work of the dramatist.
The historian's task is much harder.
The dramatist sees how all things connect,
The isolated is part of the whole,
His own spirit is part of the picture.
If unity's lacking, he invents it.
He digests the past, and reinvents it
In a single aesthetic harmony.
He's got the gist, the artistic purpose,
But this has nothing to do with justice.
To do justice to the past is harder.
That's why Grillparzer said, 'What is history
But the way we comprehend events
Forever impenetrable to us?'
Weathered by intellectual beauty,
An absolute nobility of soul
Undisfigured by the least hint of want,
The just and genuine historian
Contemplates the story of history
As though it has never been told before.
He tells it so simply, and so profoundly,
Simplicity is lost in profundity,
And profundity in simplicity.
If history is the story of time
Misconstrued, which leads us into error,
The story of time must be told again.

4

Any religion which comes to be ruled

By historical knowledge alone,
And thinks to administer justice
Solely by the rulebook of history,
Degenerates to scholarship and law.
When Christianity, for example,
Subverts and degrades the spirit of Christ,
The innocent, believing man, seeing
All the lies, absurd tricks, and cruelties
Practised in the name of Christian love,
Clings to faith against his better judgement.
  If Bach, Mozart, or Beethoven succumb
To the laws of historical science,
Music dies the death of a thousand cuts,
A thousand impertinent questions: the knife
Disguised as historical criticism.
Too much science kills art. Yet even so,
When transfigured into a work of art,
The scientific vision liberates
The very understanding it preserves.
  The lucid, dispassionate scientist
Knows science is that form of poetry
In which reason and imagination
Act together synergistically.
He takes the way of the philosopher,
Which, even if it fails, sustains his pride,
His natural dignity, and the thought,
Like a luminous fringe touching all things,
That this is the way of knowledge, not faith. .
  He links the intuition and insight
Of faith through imaginative belief,
With the reason and checkability
Of knowledge through critical acumen.
The imagination of poetry
Joins with the criticism of poetry
To illuminate the world as it is.
It follows, therefore, that just as the act

Of imagination helps to improve
The poetic vision, so does the act
Of critical judgement, based on reason.
If, then, imagination is the force
Of poetry, so, also, is science.
I see the two like the opposed muscles
Uplifting the depressing fingertips
Skedaddling piano keys to make music.
When the historical sense dominates
The very atmosphere in which we love,
Any thoughts, other than those dictated
By the regiment of historic fact,
Are dismissed, to wither as illusions.
Yet everything that lives, whether a seed,
A person, or a nation, needs illusion,
A carefree envelope of soft blue sky,
To wrap around itself and protect it
On the long, hard haul to maturity.
Anything which compels our souls to love
Less than unconditionally, severs
At the root, the source of our greatest strength.
We dry up, that is, become dishonest.
'The future is the image of the past.
A ruler is placed on two points in time,
A line is drawn, the future is mapped out.
There is nothing to debate. Anyone
Who disagrees with history is shot.'
If history is the story of time
Misconstrued, which leads us into error,
The story of time must be told again.

5

The more we come to believe history
Is the true story of the way things are,
The more readily we convince ourselves
We're living in the rearguard of mankind.

We think of ourselves, from childhood onwards,
As dutiful, if rich, inheritors
Of a time-honoured, an adult culture,
Magnificent in its sublimity,
But nearing old age, and us with it.
  Prematurely grey and backward-looking,
We walk with stiff gait and self-importance.
Our serious work is totting up the facts
Balancing the account sheets of former times.
We take consolation in past glories.
We are old, in fact, before we are young.
  Is the thought that we're passing through our prime
To our old age possibly a throwback
To the medieval theology
Of the World's End and the Last Judgement?
Life as an eschatological fact?
The same idea, perhaps, in a new dress?
  A profound sense of hopelessness remains.
Living in the shadow of history,
How may we escape the fact that we die?
  The poet Wilhelm Wackernagel said,
'We Germans are now a nation of heirs.
We have been remade out of a new past
Inherited from the immortal air
Of Classical Greece, and the equally
Immortal air of Christianity.
Even those who are hostile to both,
Admit the two new inheritances
Dominate the life of German culture.
We openly confess how, without them,
Seeing our reflection in the old Gods,
Wotan, and the ancient worship of war,
There is precious little to encourage
Spiritual life in the German tribes.'
The old man died in 1869.
  We are called on to master and surpass

The spirit of Rome and Alexander.
And if we do, to our surprise, we find,
In the great fifth century before Christ,
In a quite unhistorical people,
Irresistible sophistication
Walking freely through the streets, triumphant
Over the abstract fact of history.
If history is the story of time
Misconstrued, which leads us into error,
The story of time must be told again.

6

Ransacking history and libraries,
Pillaging just enough hard scholarship
And book knowledge for credibility,
We discover how well *irony* works;
When this wears thin, we try out *cynicism*;
At last, moving from lesser to greater,
We capitulate to the God *ego*.
We see this as practical and prudent.
After all, since we struggle to exist,
Why not get right down to it and make sure?
Egotism becomes God. True selfishness
Transfigures reality at a stroke.
Irony and *cynicism* receive us:
'Nothing will survive in time forever.
Decay and death are inevitable.
We accept the fact. We also admit
The inner strength to surrender our lives
To its irredeemable mechanism.
Hasn't Hegel made the point obvious?
The right-thinking person is the true heir
Of his indubitable World Process.
We all feel the same ecstatic release
As our spirits surrender to the truth
Of biological evolution

As the most natural thing in the world.
Why resist it? Generations of facts,
From plant, animal, and mineral worlds,
Make the point abundantly obvious.
Hasn't Darwin's *Origin of Species*
Made the point abundantly obvious?
Even in the violence of the sea
Aboriginal slime participates
In the same pyramidic World Process
Modern man stands on, at the very top,
High and proud, the Ego of Creation.'
  Hegelism and Darwinism combine
To make man, that funny little worm,
That infinitesimal atom, rant
And rave in this presumptuous manner.
Wholly divorced from the cultural style
And classic genius of antiquity,
European man courts catastrophe
Creating an egotistical God
Out of his tireless historicising.
  Ancient philosophies of becoming,
The flux of being, species, and all things,
The lack of definitive distinction
Between animal and man: I find these
Doctrines, which the Darwinist makes his own,
Quite possibly true, but nonethemore deadly.
Even believed by a generation
Possessing greater rage for instruction
Than our own, such deadly doctrines extol
Crass functionalism, greed, and the law
Of the survival of the fittest,
Which justifies any atrocity.
  This is the hour of our greatest peril.
The most alarming prospect is the young.
Cut off, at the root, from their best instincts,
Their fire, defiance, selflessness, and love;

Taught to despise a cautious maturing
In favour of speedy obedience;
Debauched of frank or strong personal feeling
To pursue the lie of the party line;
Ridiculed of their fairest privilege
Of making a great idea greater yet:
Is it any wonder we make monsters
Of the young, if we teach them such doctrines?
   If history is the story of time
Misconstrued, which leads us into error,
The story of time must be told again.

7

When young, imagination is freedom,
Because, no matter how hard it is to live,
To go on without it is to be dead.
Aesthetics chained to history, therefore,
Are a form of cultural suicide.
If youth did not possess clairvoyant gifts
For seeing through to the far side of pain,
How would my own have come to recognise
That excess of history (whether in
Public or private life) is an error
Where a paradise of health has been lost?
   The freely-moving, cultivated man
Stands opposed to the pedantic scholar,
The proud, morally-neutral scientist,
And the historico-aesthetical
Cultural philistine. He stands for life.
We see the domination of his mind
Over what has happened to him in the past.
We see the organic growth of the whole
In the clear light of normal circumstance.
   The antidote to too much history
Is the power and art of forgetting.
We love, sleep, take up a hobby, gamble,

Drink wine, withdraw to community life,
Or breathe in a bubble philosophy
Serenely independent of the times.
A second and loftier antidote
Is the contemplation of the eternal,
The extinguishable light of life
Seen through the glass of art and religion.
We learn to recognise our origin
And destination outside appearance.

8

Because all scientific proof is proved
In the light of historical knowledge,
Or discovers it's not science at all,
Scientists cannot, by definition,
Observe the eternal. They are confined
Within the logical experiment
Prescribed by scientific history.
So, since this is a specialisation,
And the part is not greater than the whole,
The terrifying dangers of science
Are therefore less than those of history.
Is history, then, to dominate life?
Or life, history? Which is the stronger force?
The Greeks learnt how to answer this; and tamed
Foreign cultures, both surrounding them
And within, like the Babylonian,
Semitic, Lydian, and Egyptian;
And grandiose religions from the East.
Struggling to keep their own identity
In the midst of such cultural chaos,
The decisive bearing the Greeks possessed
Was the Oracle of the God Apollo
In the Temple at Delphi. This gave them
Their vital, suprahistorical view,
And unity in their cultural style.

By following the Delphic Oracle,
The Greeks learnt how to organise chaos
Both in the world outside and the world within.
In every case the teaching was the same:
'Think back to yourself. What do you really want?'
Summarised in the two words, 'Know yourself.'
Objective and subjective fact became
The contemplation of the universe.
The spurious need was dissipated.
'The Greek' was one aim in search of itself
Through all the various pursuits of life,
Whether marketing, thinking, making art,
Or the political will of the state.
It was this undivided unity
In the Greek moral conscience which gave them
Unparalleled superiority
Over the rival cultures of their time.
Creating high culture out of chaos,
The Greeks took possession of this wisdom,
The firstborn and model of all who come
To understand the word *European*.
If history is the story of time
Misconstrued, which leads us into error,
The story of time must be told again.

The Dream of Intelligence:7

Like a pregnant nucleus of white fire
Articulating pure intelligence
Out of the supreme effortlessness of love,
I had, since childhood, seen the mystical,
The terror-crystalled courts outside the world,
In which even my own mind was found wanting.
I wanted a mind, set in my mind's eye,
To inculcate the perfect example.
I wanted a mind as educator
To be the model for my lifetime's work.
Schopenhauer? Wagner? It was not to be.
  I showed a majestic indifference
To all the social idols then upheld,
Popular culture, Christianity,
Success, money, status, Bismarck, The Reich,
Pointing up the individual aim
Greek self-discipline self-generated.
  Where I am today, what I am today,
High on this existential mountain peak,
Where I spear less with words than with lightning,
Ah, how utterly beyond my targets then!
Yet I kept my feet on the ground. Not once
Did I deceive myself by mapping out
A safe but boring route through my career.
I took one step at a time, but took it
Through Germany, Switzerland, Italy,
Over the mountains and down to the sea,
  There is a grand, sedentary repose
Speaking the volume of a person's worth.
I reached this, happy to gaze the future,
Conscious I would now fulfil my purpose.

I wrote, I know, certain words which drip blood,
Anxious to inflict the wounds they suffered;
But, through art, an animating spirit
Like a summer breeze, caresses them all,
Soothing, 'Terrors, wounds, mortality,
Do not act as an objection to life.'

2

I understood the core of my doctrine
Had explosive force, making everyone
And everything a target in its range.
For I was forging philosophy distinct
From school groups, including even a Kant,
Not to mention academic ruminants
Cowed to the bullheads of philosophy.

3

When I remember how I lived my life
In those days, practising the scholar's craft
So conscientiously it could be said
I actually knew something about it,
The skilled emergence of a flint-chipped spark
Feeling out the darkness of the scholar
To write my books, touches me profoundly,
Now I review the pathos of distance.
What self-assurance I possessed!
The treacherous distance yet to travel
Through men and women, war, and minor works,
Before the mighty words could hit the mark,
Haunts me even now that I have crossed it.
There is a prudence in the simple truth.
Oh, I had many faces, many rôles,
Before each face and rôle became the man
I am, consummated in my labours.
And so, for a while, I was a scholar.

4

The development of my intellect
Was soon challenged to the point of crisis.
Human, All-Too-Human commemorates,
In a worthy monument of a book,
The tortuous mentalities outlived.
Every word inveigles a reader towards
An irreversible enlightenment...
  Free spirit means nothing other to me
Than someone to whom nothing is taboo.
We are free, if we take it on ourselves,
To witness Virtue prostitute herself,
Or Vice undress to embrace her true love.
Morals are the staff not the boss of mind.
The enlightened soul comes into being
The day it takes possession of itself.
  Cold, savage, hard, incisive, mocking, wise,
My tone, my voice, now changed completely.
The more I sniff *Human, All-Too-Human*,
The more I smell a sharp, snouty power
Nosing out the cozy homes and bolt-holes
Of all ideals' secret security vaults:
The still grain in stone cellars, the barrels
Of olive oil, the sacks of diamonds
Leaning on dusty walls, the greased rifles
Stacked to the ceiling in wooden boxes,
Padlocked illuminated manuscripts,
Racked paintings, crystal, silverware, baskets
Of rubies, emeralds, pearls, uncut stones,
The gold ingots stockpiled in locked barracks.
The full inventory exhausts belief,
Cataloguing the other side of dreams,
The idealists' anti-ideal coffers.
  In the cool, steady cone of a torchlight,
I explored this underworld of ideals.
This was war, but war without gunpowder.

Here were no bayonets, cannon, bullets
Flying the battlefield like mad ideas.
All that would have been ideals. On my part.
   One after another all the ideals
Were laid to rest. Observed by one condemned,
They froze to stone in the ice of my gaze.
The hero froze; the genius; the saint;
And pity was chilled to the bone. The pure
Things-in-themselves of Kantian logic,
Like soft rain turning into snowflakes, froze.
   I was on the *via negativa*.

5

The crisis, and how it resolved itself,
Was not simply my divorce from Wagner.
The danger was more serious than that.
Total aberration of instinct
Was what I had survived. The blunders,
Like Wagner and the Basle Professorship,
Were mere symptoms. The stronger I became,
The more I realised it was high time
I got on with the purpose of my life.
   I look back on a desert of ten years:
I've forgotten more than I remember
Suppering on dust for scholarship's sake.
Scrupulously following with the nail
Of my finger, to focus bad eyesight,
I forced my life for ten years through antique metrists
Becoming the thing I wasn't. It pains me,
It tortures me now, to relive those years
When I abandoned myself to that fate.
None of my work touched my predicament.
Not one of my ideals knew the way out.
   Burning thirst tormented then possessed me.
I was unable to apply myself
To studies weightier than medicine,

Physiology, or natural science –
Not even the study of history.
This was the period I understood
The deadly connection between a job
Laughing in the face of a man's nature,
And the irresistible attraction,
Addiction, craving, and lust for a drug
To stupefy resentment's void, and gorge
Burning thirst on chemical narcosis.
  Or mythic, transubstantiating art,
Like Richard Wagner's art, for example.
  I saw the primary violation
Of nature, ignoring instinct, almost
Compelled the secondary addiction.

6

Any kind of life was better than that
Terrible trap, unrelenting selflessness,
Into which I fell, into which I walked:
I was turning into somebody else.
Working in poverty, in jail, I thought
Infinitely preferable to that.
Any kind of life was better than that.

7

In my private mind I had always known
How Karl, my father, had been doomed to die.
Now the same physiological traits
Were slowly, imperceptibly, freeing me
From the formal obligations to my job.
I was more than ready to accept this,
I was inwardly relieved, even as
Sickness grappled and possessed my body.
  On May the 2nd, 1879,
At the age of 34½,
I handed in my formal resignation.

I was awarded, because of my health,
An annual pension of 3000 francs,
Paid out jointly by the Swiss Government
And Basle University. I was free.

8

Out of my blood went the heady vapours
Of all ideals, all beautiful feelings,
The nuance with its cloudy poetry;
In short, all the lofty swindles I'd seen
Infecting my contemporaries' brains.
The main body of the book was written
In the winter of 1876
Lodged in a villa in Italy
Fifteen minutes' walk outside Sorrento.
Two colleagues, Paul Rée and Albert Brenner,
Were there, equally glad to be writing.
Paul's *Psychological Observations*,
Published the year before, had impressed me;
And Albert was a youthful novelist.
Our hostess, Malwida von Maysenbug,
Who rented the villa, had asked us to stay.
She lived upstairs and cooked the daily meals.
We lived downstairs and could see from the lounge
Beyond the olive grove in the front garden
Gazing out over the Bay of Naples
The changing lights on Mount Vesuvius.
We met up in the lounge after supper
To sit and talk; or Paul would read aloud
From Herodotus or Thuycidides,
The New Testament, Montaigne, Rochefoucauld,
Stendhal, or Burckhardt's lectures on the Greeks.
For six months we lived our common dream
In this monastery for free spirits
As I called it. Surrounded by villas,
Each secluded behind high-walled gardens

Of peach, pear, pine, cedar, cypress, and vine,
The *Villa Rubinacci* was a part
Of the timeless Italian landscape.
We lived together happily till spring.
  The final draft of the book was written
The following winter in Switzerland
Under much less propitious circumstances.
Though still teaching, I was in constant pain.
My devoted colleague, Herr Peter Gast
The composer, studying then in Basle,
Declared *my* book to be on *his* conscience.
With bandages wound around my head and jaw,
And headaches hammering, I dictated
While he wrote or corrected. The fact was
He wrote it. I was simply the author.
  When, later on, the printed book arrived,
I was so ill I didn't recognize
How it had anything to do with me.
Nevertheless, I sent out copies to friends,
Who included the Wagners in Bayreuth.

9

Was it coincidence? Or miracle?
Or chance? At precisely this period,
A de luxe edition of *Parsifal*
Arrived through the post signed by The Master:
'For his dear friend, Friedrich Nietzsche,
Richard Wagner, Church Councillor.' Well, well,
The crossing of the two books resounded
As if not books but steel swords had crossed!
We haunted each other with silence.
Incredible! Wagner had become pious.

10

I declared war on morality.
My next book, *The Dawn*, emphasized the point.

Not that it smelt in the least of gunpowder.
To anyone with a nose for subtlety,
It has a gentle, aromatic scent.
It's a happy sea-animal of a book,
Sleek and round, sunning itself on the rocks.
On any analysis, this is me.
Almost every sentence in the book
Was thought, was fished out of the rocky shore
Close to Genoa, where I lived alone
Often in communion with the sea.
'Many are the days that have not yet dawned':
These words from the Indian *Rig Veda*
I inscribed over the entrance to the book.
So where did I look for the hint of dawn
Or the redeeming light of the future?
In liberation from morality.
In revaluation of all values.
This sun-loving book was a source of light,
Of tenderness, of love, towards the shunned.
It gave them back their soul, their good conscience,
Their privilege, and their right to exist.
Morality wasn't attacked, simply
Removed from the centre of attention.
I asked if we too, steering westward, dare
Reach New Indias, even if we are
Shipwrecked on the coasts of infinity?

11

The purpose of my life was now to scour
The foundations of the mind long enough
To capture one truly *divine lizard*:
Mankind watching itself confront at high noon
The past, present, and future, holding time
In the gaze of its own serenity;
Taking in, once and for all, the riot
Of chance and the domination of creed.

We are not, by ourselves, on the right road.
We are, by no means, divinely directed.
Our instinct for decadence has found out
Its most seductive court and ruling place
Exactly among our divine values,
Exactly among our holiest thoughts.
The unconscious urge we have to believe
Everything is really in the right hands;
The unconscious urge we have to believe
There is a book called *The Holy Bible*,
Which will set our minds at rest forever;
The unconscious urge we have to believe
Divinely ordained Government rules us:
This, translated back into reality,
Is nothing other than the unconscious wish
To suppress and annihilate the truth,
Which is, in fact, the very opposite.
Namely, the government of mankind
Has consistently been in the wrong hands.
Governed by the sly, the underprivileged,
The truth-haters, the anarchistic mobs,
The cunning, the proud seekers of revenge,
The mediocre and the violent,
It's a miracle we've survived at all.

12

When an organ fails to conserve itself,
No longer replacing lost energy,
Damaged tissue and membranes; when it fails
To restore a unique identity
To health's quick and assured self-interest,
The organ and the whole disintegrate.
For a physiologist, weighing up
Probable loss of the whole, or the loss
Of corruption in a damaged organ,
There can be no question of sympathy,

Of solidarity with frailty,
Or pity for the loss of half a leg.
Keeping his mind and his eye on the task,
He cuts out the gangrene with a scalpel.
The priest, by contrast, welcomes the gangrene,
The grevious mortification of man.
With this precisely, our rotting bodies,
Scarcely alive, yet still breathing, he keeps
His domination on humanity.
This is why he cultivates emotions
Which magnify the scale of our helplessness.
When contempt for the body politic,
Disguised as salvation of the soul, gains
The mandate of the state, what is this but
The perfect recipe for disaster?

13

A poem which expresses gratitude
For the most wonderful January
I ever knew (my next book was its gift),
Indicates out of what geodic depths
The scientific method is happy.

Der du mit dem Flammenspeere
Meiner Seele Eis zerteilt,
Dass sie brausend nun zum Meere
Ihrer höchsten Hoffnung eilt:

Heller stets und stets gesunder,
Frei im liebevollsten Muss –
Also preist sie deine Wunder,
Schönster Januarius!

As if I'd been pierced by a hot beam of light,
That sacred month cut me open alive.
I was a glacier melting into seas

Tossing exotic plumes, then riding high
Down through volcanic cliffs out to the calm
Oceanic stillness, tropical guitars
Welcomed across the water, the stencilled palms
Fanning the stars in dawn's quiet praise.
  Crystallized under ferocious pressure,
The words, the first words of *Zarathustra*,
Shattered me: '*Incipit tragedia*,
The tragedy begins.' I was confronted
By the voice of my own unconscious mind:
'*Who is evil? Who puts someone to shame.*
Who is human? Who saves someone from shame.
Who is enlightened? Who frees shame itself.'

The Dream of Intelligence:8

And so, at last, the time has come for me
To tell the story of *Zarathustra.*
It concerns our philosophical need
When the best or the worst happens to us.
What is my actual philosophy
When I am faced with the best or the worst?
Amor fati? The love of fate? To feel
That though I might, or might not, have wanted
This particular event to occur,
It has in fact occurred, and does exist –
And warrants my love as a part of life?
Or do I deny it tells me anything,
In any shape or form whatsoever,
And forge a militant intelligence
Never budging from love or hate for it?
  Dare I see the best lasting forever
Without wanting to be a part of it?
Dare I see the worst lasting forever
Without wanting to put a stop to it?
Dare I try to love the fate of the world?
  Dare I propose, in all seriousness,
The true philosophical attitude,
Outfacing the temptation of pleasure
Or the greater temptation of control,
Is an *amor fati*, a love of fate,
Such that, by loving fate, no matter what
Hell or heaven tortures or attends me
In my body, my conscience, or my soul
Through change and flux, flux and change unchanging,
I may in the end inherit – life?
  I dare propose, in all seriousness,

The true philosophical attitude
Contemplates an eternal recurrence
Of all values, whether good or evil,
Throughout time, in all the changes time brings,
Such that, whatever happens, whatever
Enters existence, such philosophy
Understands it is not condemned to rot,
Damned to tread an eternal nightmare wheel
Of repetition of the same events,
But of their characteristic values,
But of their good or evil. I perceive
This distinction as characteristic
Of what is out-, and what is inside, mind,
And so liberate myself from my mind.
Watch this world of mental values: it is
A sculpted sphere, a colossal planet,
A stone revolving in perpetuity,
Showing, as though worked by an inner hand,
The natural world in all its glory,
The lilies of the field of Jesus, seas,
The growth of living things and their decay, –
From animals swallowing animals
Alive, to the calm of a rose garden, –
A sculpted sphere, a colossal planet,
A stone revolving in perpetuity,
A world come to terms with itself, breathing
The everlasting force inside the sphere,
The everlasting force inside the wisdom
Of the psychology of tragedy:
My aesthetic vision of life itself.

2

I teach the high heart and the love of life.
The first experience I had of this
Belongs to August 1881.
I was living then in Sils-Maria

In a small boarding-house in the Swiss Alps.
One fine day I was walking through the woods
Close by the banks of Lake Silvaplana,
When I came to a rock two metres high
Shaped like a pyramid, not far from Surlei
Between the footpath and the water's edge.
Sensing an uncanny silence, I stopped:
Eternal recurrence struck me, like lightning
Radiating my being to the core.

3

Scored for a mixed chorus and orchestra,
My *Hymn to Life* was also written then.
This graphic tracing of my condition
At such an acute turning-point in my life,
When the pathos of living out both sides
Of the comedy and tragedy of life
Was unbearably alive within me,
Cannot possibly be dismissed as trite.
The time may even come when people will say,
'This is what we sing in his memory.'
The text, I must state explicitly,
Is not by me, but the inspiration
Of a young Russian woman, my friend then,
Lou von Salomé. Anyone who feels
Any poetry or pathos in it
Will know why I admire and respect it:
She achieves the vision of tragedy.
Listen to her words as she speaks to life,
'If it is true happiness is dead,
Come, I do not mind, give me your pain.'
Perhaps my music also at this point,
United with her words, touches greatness?

4

How clearly I remember her saying

'I never thought it would be possible
Experience of such joy and sorrow
Could ever reach through to another soul.
But now, knowing you, I know I was wrong.
I feel a boundless union dawning
On the golden horizon of our joined lives.'
'From what bright star have we fallen to meet here?'
I asked, loving her as I loved the soul
Of the world she was loving me then.
She was, without doubt, the most brilliant mind
At ease in the body of a woman
It has ever been my pleasure to know.
Yet out of the fate it was mine to bear,
Intellectual vanity betrayed
Her more than heavenly, her Godly soul.
For she, aswish with my astonished friends
(And years later she was still a virgin),
Boasted of conquering my heart and mind,
Flaunting her victory in my circle,
Even that around Wagner in Bayreuth!
I couldn't marry such pride, and broke off
All formal approaches to the prospect.
Yet I never ceased to love the woman
Who forelived with me, high above Orta,
On the monte sacro of Saint Francis,
The just and full measure of uncontrolled
Dionysian sexuality.

5

It was not long before the influence
Of loving so remarkable a woman
And losing her to herself, opened me
To high noon and *Thus Spoke Zarathustra*.
It was the child of our joined intellects,
Great brother to our first, the *Hymn to Life*.
By the way, there's a misprint in the *Hymn*.

The last note of the clarinet in A
Is printed as C. It should be C flat.

6

When winter came I moved to Rapallo
Living in its charming, secluded bay,
That little world of forgotten happiness
Scooped out of hills not far from Genoa.
My condition had worsened. The winter
Was cold, damp, and oppressively rainy.
I lodged in a small hotel by the sea
Where the high waves made sleep frantic at best,
The very opposite of a retreat.
Yet, almost as a proof that all great works
Which live, come into being 'in spite of',
It was winter, with my health sickening,
When *Zarathustra* came into being.
  I walked, in the mornings, to the south-east
Through pine above the panoramic sea
Climbing the mountainous road to Zoagli.
Whenever my body felt up to it,
I walked, in the afternoons, to the south-west
Around the bay to Santa Margherita,
On to the headland at Porto Fino,
Turning to stride the five kilometres home.
  It was on these morning and afternoon walks
The frenzy of poetry first seized me.
I wrote down the words in the open air
With terrifying zest, even in the rain.
So perhaps I should say, *it possessed me*...

7

Anybody with a serious soul,
Who wants to experience the compass
Of values and desiderata,
Who will know from his own experience

Just what it means to come to terms with death,
Whoever wants to know how a saint feels,
Or an artist, or scientist, or judge,
Or a wise, or pious man, or a divine
Old hermit living apart from the world,
Like a medieval ambassador
In the corrupt warzone of the present, –
Will have one courage above all others,
The great health, as often as it is lost.
  We, the true Argonauts of the ideal,
Whose courage, perhaps, outstrips our patience,
Who've been shipwrecked and hurt often enough,
But are, as I say, the healthier for it,
It seems to us, as if, as a reward,
We tread at last the undiscovered country
No map or compass dares to envision:
  'O clear vision of the ideal spirit
Of man, woman, and child in divine play
With all the objects ever called holy,
Intercede, O let us, O let us hold you
One moment in the passing of our lives,
One moment in the passing of our lives
Neither knowingly nor possessively
But out of superabundance of love
And the power of spontaneity.'

8

Is there anyone with a clear idea
Of what poets in the strong ages called
Inspiration? I'll try to define it.
If I were slightly more superstitious
I'd be tempted by the proposition
A poet is no more than the mouthpiece,
The bodily medium incarnate,
Of the impersonal force of language
Abusing him to get itself written.

But, as it is, the idea that something
With subtle yet unmistakable force
Takes on visibility, emits sound,
Stunning the shocked receiver to the depths,
Illustrates no more than a particle.
A poet hears, without contriving, the words.
He conducts them, without knowing their source:
As, charged with necessity of itself,
Thought flashes into being, and, like lightning,
Lights up the dark acreage of the mind.
No poet is blind to the power of words,
(Least of all those which appear to have none.)
Yet raptures whose tremendous tensions sing
Out of the joy of joy, discharge at times
Into the rain of tears, and sorrows' pool.
The poet is not exactly in charge.
Lithe with insight or jinxed by goose pimples,
Sometimes less, though often more, than himself,
He frequently exists outside himself,
Shuddering slightly to watch himself write.
He's in a kind of happiness at depth
In which the lonely flowers on the graves
Of those who gave him life now give him death
Do not oppose, or challenge, but provoke,
Condition, and demand – necessitate
A superabundant light in the world
Revealing them as part of what it is.
Struck dumb in the glut of death, the blood and hair,
The instinct for rhythmic relationships
Alone provides the bearings which inspire.
Rhythm is like a bridge. It spans the gap
Between the establishment and vision.
Geared to the mud, yet tossed in airborne steel,
An acrobat in stern geometry,
A bridge, in fact, is objective rhythm.
The instinct for rhythmic relationships

Interarches the impossible truth.
The wider the overleaps, the wider
The measure of the length of inspiration,
The span of the rolling rhythm's touchdown
Counteracting each pressure and tension.
In the highest sense imaginable,
Poetry occurs because it has to.
The words emerge like the smile of freedom,
Absolute freedom, and the power of life.
Perhaps the strangest phenomenon
Engineering a poet, is the making
Of metaphors in the unconscious mind.
As he labours, the metaphors emerge
Removed from any thought of the author
Out of the pure simplicity of themselves.
Or again, trying to write, the poet
Has long since given up any attempt
To find what is, or is not, the right word,
The just, the appropriate, metaphor;
When, suddenly, deeper than intention,
He is the sluice and conduit of truth
Through whom the waters of language hurtle
To irrigate the sween green plains with words.
How? Metaphor is reaped as rich as this
Because of the springs of inspiration.
Now it is they come and caress your page
Regardless of their worth or worthlessness,
Flattering you, hoping for a free ride.
Dying to live, they signal from the flames
Of Pandora's Box, pledging you the truth.
The key to the word chest burns in your hands.
All you have to do is open the lock.
Being desires to become your language.
Becoming itself wants to be your words.
This is my knowledge of inspiration.
There's just a chance, thousands of years ago,

I heard a small voice whisper, 'And mine too.'

9

After I had experienced in full
The ferocity of poetic frenzy,
I was ill for two weeks in Genoa.
Then came a melancholy spring in Rome
Putting up with life, which wasn't easy.
Rome for the poet of *Zarathustra*
Was the worst possible place to be.
  I found the city grim and depressing.
I hadn't, in fact, wanted to be there.
I had tried to settle in L'Aquila,
Eighty kilometres to the northeast.
Built in honour of that atheist,
The great Hohenstaufen Emperor
Frederick the Second, by his son Conrad,
L'Aquila was founded in 1250
A blatant counterconcept to Rome
Openly hostile to the Papacy.
But the crucial decisions were not mine
And I was forced to travel back to Rome.
  After exhausting myself uselessly
Trying to find antichristian quarters,
I finally came to terms with my fate
Lodged in the Piazza Barberini.
I'm sorry to say that before I did,
In order to avoid the bad odours
Of the city as much as possible,
I asked at the official residence
Of the King himself, in the Palazzo
Del Quirinale, for a suitable room
To accommodate a philosopher!
  High above the Piazza Barberini,
Walking a gallery open to the air,
Gazing out over the Roman rooftops

Towards the lights and stars in the distance,
I composed the loneliest song I know,
Or have written, *The Night Song*, as the folds
Of the fountains splashed in the streets below.
And as I wrote, I heard a melody,
Immovable in its melancholy,
Murmur such mental ardour within me,
It had forever wanted a refrain.
And in my song I heard its lone refrain:
'I am dying of immortality.'

10

I took power, suppleness, and euphony,
And with them forged a new poetic line.
Perhaps modesty should restrain me here?
All I will say is that while composing
I became aware I had probably
Brought the German language to a new
Zenith of perfection. After Luther,
After Goethe, a third stage was called for.
More severe and masculine than Goethe,
Without however condescending to
The coarse mob gutterals of Luther,
My *Zarathustra* is a dance, a play
Revelling in the skills of symmetry,
Yet vaulting and mocking them all the same.
I have been a poet to the limits.
To find my own truth or falsehood of heart,
I have tyrannized over myself so thoroughly
With the obverse of everything called poetic
Till only the unconquerable words arose.

11

Inspired by the kingfisher skies of Nice,
And Lou Salomé, I finished the poem.
The closing dithyrambs were written down

Exactly at that timeless moment when
Half past three in the afternoon
Tolled along the cold canals of Venice
The sacred hour of Richard Wagner's death.
Lost in the pine trees where the winter sun
Striates the trunks across the needled floor;
Or startled partridge, frightened to a bough,
Dusts the silence throughout a golden hour;
Or stark on a rock, dizzy amid gorse,
Compounded out of fossils, but now live
In being's roar, my head the ball of fire
Ten thousand sunsets bandied on the sea:
I have seen such glories surrounding Nice
To consecrate my memory forever.
A lone observer would have seen me walking,
Or dancing, seven or eight hours a day
On the Alpine Mountains, laughing out loud,
By, to, at myself; for those were the days
I slept well at night; for those were the days
Vigour and patience found true union.
Nor is it possible I will forget
That sacred moment when I stopped to write
On the Old and the New Tablets of the Law
Halfway up the hazardous, stifling climb
Beyond the railway station to that marvellous
Moorish castle on the heights at Eza.

12

One pays dearly for immortality.
One pays dearly to write an immortal book.
One dies at least three times before one's death.
Something I call the rancour of the great
First turns against the maker of greatness
The backlash of revenge. And rancour smells
Of bitter and inveterate hatred
Towards everything to do with greatness.

Precisely because greatness was achieved,
There is nothing new to look forward to;
And yet one cannot face life without it;
Or faces it pale, weak from achievement.
That which *wasn't even willed* lies in the past,
Now immortal, one's name attached to it.
Now it is necessary to labour
Under its weight, which can crush the greatest,
This weight I call the rancour of the great.
   Then there is the silence of one's peers,
Even more disturbing in solitude.
Then go out and meet people. Call on friends.
This makes the silence the more desolate yet.
Nobody recognizes your spirit.
Nobody greets you with a knowing eye.
At best, unilateral revulsion
Throughout the spectrum of intensity.
   Nobility of soul, which cannot breathe
Without venerating upwards, reveres,
Therefore, those whom the ignoble despise.
Ignoble people find this offensive:
It hits them as a judgement of themselves.
And so it is, that in society,
The barrier between the noblest of souls,
And the rest, creates the pathos of distance:
Downwards or upwards, the vision is grim,
Measuring the scale of human despair.
And who will thank you for placing him there?
   The third kind of dying prematurely –
An absurd susceptibility of heart
To inconsequential remarks, groaning
Under insignificant strokes of fate –
Works precisely because it is absurd.
If some hesitate to destroy the great,
The instincts of poisonous flies do not.
All the small things assume awesome power.

The reason for this loss of armour
Stems from the tremendous energy consumed
In the rigours of the creative act.
Burning in the furnaces of making,
The innermost core of tender being
Gracing a line of molten poetry
Exacts the same order of energy
As rougher souled and hardy men employ
Forging rods of incandescent steel.

13

Thus Spoke Zarathustra is world-historic.
Dionysian in the extreme, there
In the wide music of the dithyramb,
That abstract concept achieves reality.
Neither Dante, nor Shakespeare, nor Goethe
Would dare despise its Dionysian air.
Nor is this all, for unlike them, I am
Both physics *and* metaphysics made new.
Dante's *Divine Comedy* decks the bones
Of a medieval theology
In terza rima dress: the Roman
Catholic heart of Thomas Aquinas,
Who presupposes astronomy and
Aristotle and Christ's vision of God.
Shakespeare's plays assume traditional form
In all the dignity of Thespian art;
And into this Dionysian mould,
With his unruly genius, he pours
The liquid gold of truth, which settles out
As ingots of a Dionysian stamp.
But if (the point unproved) history states,
'No! William Shakespeare's immortal plays
Are strictly in the liturgical mould
Die-cast and hammered by The Early Church!',
This proves, like Dante, his logic's Christian.

Goethe's mind, too, champions the dark clouds
Of religious and medieval myth,
Culminating in the figure of Faust
Shot through by the stormy sun of science,
Itself an adjunct to philosophy,
The most truthful of the sciences.

14

Anaxagoras was banned from Athens
For stating the sun was not a god
But a sphere of flame. Socrates killed himself
Drinking the hemlock supplied by the courts
Of a jittery Athens – to keep faith
With the spirit of Greek philosophy.
Giordano Bruno was burnt at the stake
(By the Roman Catholic Church) for holding
The astronomy of Copernicus
To be closer to the truth than Ptolemy's;
While Galileo, under house arrest,
Was almost burned alive for the same thing.
One fine day, Descartes, unconvinced by all
Theological bullies, rethought thought,
And tried to get back to how anything
Could be thought to be true in the first place.
Cogito ergo sum. Immortal words!
I think therefore I am. He makes logic
Dazzlingly free of the will to the end
Characteristic of the tyrannous.
The Greek philosophical tradition,
Therefore, presupposes revolution
Against any system of government
Which seeks to impose established thought
On the fundamental freedom of the mind.
None of the same heroism for truth
Distinguishes the oriental record.
On the contrary, the eastern thinker

Displays a genius for evasion
And frank disavowal of the brute facts.
As witness the stern *Bhagavad-Gita*
Sanctifying fratricide in the cause
Of an abstract, sacred metaphysics:
I raise this finger, which lifts my trumpets,
Slams my cymbals, hoots my conch shells, uprearing
Plumed white horses snorting rhetoric
Unleashing the steel chariots of war!
The philosophy of the ruling priest
As warlord here finds apotheosis.
Or molten lead was poured into the ears
Of strangers, who, by accident or chance,
Had heard the words of the holy *Vedas*.
What Indian thinker stood up to this?
  And vast though its lore in self-awareness,
Essential to individuation
And psychological growth of the soul,
The limits of the self became the limits
Of external enquiry; while conscience
Forgave itself on the grounds of impotence.
  The flow of oriental thought compares
With Christian thought in the middle ages,
From the introspection of the Desert Fathers,
Through the mythology of the holy grail,
Down to the time of Thomas Aquinas
And the majesty of the great cathedrals.
There was no categoric enquiry,
No permanent, no incessant feedback
With the methods of natural science.
Men of genius devoted their lives
To making maps and charts of their own minds.
Drinking cosmic energy at the source,
They by-passed the cities of life. Yogis
Turned their attention inwards to explore
The mansions of the mind (its floors, its doors):

Nothing is conceivable except mind.
Self is the Seer, mind belongs to the seen.
Now the dying round the holy power.
Indian philosophy is like God
Exacting a mutation in the soul.
When the people lose access to the truth
Through spectacular disregard for it
And shameless flattery of sacred books,
Truth itself is a political dead duck.
Thus, what eastern country has not despaired
Researching its own past to discover
Need of the scientific tradition
Born of free, western Greek philosophy?
Because Zarathustra did not exist,
It was necessary to invent him.

15

There's a terrifying truth to the mind,
No matter how we choose to look at it,
Which is, contrary to civilized wish,
The noblest art and the wisest science
Act as passive instruments of evil.
There is no work it cannot serve evil,
Which is the real horror of the term.
Civilization, therefore, feels betrayed
Watching its highest ideals serve the worst;
And asks by what strength or logic
Man may overthrow evil energy.
This is why the origin of evil
Out of the light of a million suns
Shining through the mask of our genius,
Is, perhaps, the most serious question
Torturing the corpse of philosophy.
I come at this from a time and place
Beyond the genesis of good and evil.
And who of those living under the roof

Of the carapace of good and evil,
Dare to look up to see me looking down
From the mountains of independent mind
On the known cities of morality?
For this is the least of it, and gives
No idea of the gratitude, of the
Azure gratitude in which I greet life.
I have looped the circle, crossed the border,
And understood the maze outside myself,
Deciphering the holy graffiti
Burning on the precincts of the perfect.
Fewer and fewer, higher and higher,
Follow, climbing the blue, the sacred mountains,
For I am creating philosophy
Out of the blue, out of the evermore
Sacred mountains, the blue, sacred mountains.
I didn't know whether to laugh or cry
Remembering my former ignorance.
But what I did now was like creating
The internal combustion of a star.
Nothing detained, distracted, nor disturbed
Profound rapture before the art of making,
Good nor evil nor the emanation
Of the radical ecstasy of things.
The beauty was, wrapt in concentration,
Terrified by, though yet terrifying,
Zarathustra's atoms of becoming,
I saw myself project morality
Onto his uncreated character!
The more I saw, the more I realised
A supreme act of self-knowledge was called for.
Transcendentally hatched out of anguish,
To fill the void of my moral despair,
I watched the birth of the man of new values,
While the old man of morals died in me.

16

And as I contemplated, I noticed
Good and evil were intrinsic functions
Of the anatomy of my own mind.
I saw how my mental anatomy,
As it radiates imagination,
Defines the good or evil of a thing.
A physical diagram of my brain
Constituted my moral prejudice!
And rapture alone had the essential eye
To guide me, disembodied, to the cells
Dividing into me before my gaze.
And so I saw how poetry is born
Out of the living tissue of the mind.

17

I fashioned Zarathustra to enloop
The great souls of the ages, threading gold
Zeroes of the mind from the start of thought.
Like an actor countermanding the chorus
In the first tragedies of Aeschylus;
Like a character out of Rabelais
Exhausting the ethics of becoming;
Like a gypsy ambling in a marketplace,
Joking with jokers, sizing up the fruit,
Tolerating enemies (say the priests
Sweating in the heat in their long black gowns
As dust swirls in the sun and tethered goats
Kick in the waggons by the squealing pigs);
Like a man descending from his tower
In the mountains of independent mind,
Zarathustra is the prototypic
Free individual in a mass age
Contradicting superabundantly
The totalitarian psychosis
And dictatorial logic of the mob.

Because Zarathustra did not exist,
It was necesary to invent him.

18

Not until the handsome fictional shape
Of happy eyes and soul-explosive clothing
On supple backbone have been taken in
And set like a stranger in a garden
Free to wander till his host returns home,
Can we appreciate the proportions
Of his animal dignity at depth,
His looks, his economy of movement,
His musical intensity of mind,
Conscious not one iota of his proud
Sexual nature will be vilified:
The Roman Caesar with the soul of Christ.
As drops of rain tumbling in a clear sky
Focus the light of day to a rainbow,
So he walks in the beams of becoming,
A human philosophical prism
Refracting the premoral radiance
Into the ethics of the Caesar Christ.

19

Any who walk beside him, walk among
Revelations inexhaustible to
The greatest sages of antiquity,
Or seers in more recent times, or now.
Necessarily more than the fireflakes
Glimpsed by the human imagination,
The radiance is the inextinguishable,
The everlasting *Fire* Heraclitus saw
Rhythmically burning existence; dying,
Flaring up, dying, flaring up; the *Fire*
Burning fire, burning purity and ash,
Burning lips and cheeks, coke and clinker, rock,

Burning rainbows, burning all foundation;
Withdrawing from us, baring all that is,
Advancing, all that is in a bonfire:
The everlasting *Fire* Hercalitus saw.
  Working like a stoker at the furnace
Imagined round this fire, the tragic poet
Works at the white heat inside the furnace,
Just like Plato made Socrates, to forge
A semiotic of the holy life.
And as he works he sings this lonely song,
'The soul who steps on the longest ladder
To heaven, who descends as far to hell;
The rapacious soul, who wants to explore
The unexamined portions of himself;
The necessary soul, who relishes
The joys of chance, of taking risks, of gambling;
The soul who, commensurate with his being,
Plunges into the fire of becoming;
The soul who possesses himself, his life,
Desiring desire, willing will; the soul
Who backs off from life, horrified by pain,
But comes to terms, discovering his true
Equilibrium in the wider sphere:
The mystical fact of life itself;
The wise soul, sweetly courted by his fools;
The soul who knows himself, who knows how soul
Seeks out soul, and loves to love the soul;
The soul through whom all souls come to being;
And shapes of men and women, merging, flow
In currents and countercurrents, ebbing
And flowing in cellular union . . . '
But this is Dionysus once again,
The reason-melting power of the heart.
'For into the abyss I will forever
Hurtle and burn, carrying my blessing
Venerating life and adoring it,

Even in the face of total horror.'
For this is the song of Dionysus.

The Dream of Intelligence:9

What I had to do in the years ahead
Lay before me with perfect clarity.
Zarathustra had taught me to accept
The philosophical necessity
Of coming to terms with worse than the worst,
Incipient insanity, my death.
It taught me the redemptive mechanism,
The wisdom of tragedy: to function
Out of negative capability,
That is, to recreate life as it is
Without worry about morality,
And so be able, extramorally,
To reflect back to view the facts of life
In the hard, concrete medium of art.
  It was my job now in life to say No
To all the corrupt people in the world,
And create the brand new world of values
Of my political philosophy.
Part of this task was to seek out people
Who thought like me; who, out of love through strength,
Wanted to annihilate corruption
At the root of the thought, wherever found.
I needed philosophical allies.
From this time onwards, all my books were hooks...
Dare I say I fished as well as any?
If forced to admit I caught nothing, well,
Who can blame me for that? There were no fish.

2

My next book, *Beyond Good and Evil*,
1886, criticised the world

We live in, excluding neither science,
Art, nor the political arena.
I did this by pointing up in outline
The man of new values, the gentleman,
As unlike the modern as possible,
Who, with his radical backbone intact,
Stood tall in the confrontation with life,
Yet at home in the spiritual world.
The book is a textbook for radicals,
A guide through the contemporary mind
It takes courage to confront, let alone
Master and digest. For it speaks to those
Not yet conditioned to react with fear
When face to face with unprecedented
Revelation of asinine make-up
Masquerading as personality
Behind the mask of one's very own face
Cutting its 'proven figure' in the world.
I drew my noble man from ancient Greece,
But new, in shocking contrast to men now.
Take 'objectivity', for example,
Idolised throughout the civilized world,
But not by those who cross the undrawn line
Beyond the edges of fashionable thought
To brave the deserts of metaphysics
'Objective' coves find inhospitable.
Take 'sympathy for each suffering thing',
Praised as compassion, which is, more often,
Self-righteous indignation stoking its
Self-pity, smouldering with impotence
To overpower the true cause of pain,
Which hurts others, and therefore hurts ourselves.
As such, it measures our powerlessness,
Which may indeed at times be infinite.
(The powerlessness, not the compassion.)
Take 'our historical sense', sensitive

And submissive before foreign cultures
No matter how disruptive, yet heady
With pride to grub pusillanimous fact,
Bowing before the scientific man.
Noble man cannot stomach such values.

3

When I take stock *Beyond Good and Evil*
Was written soon after *Zarathustra*,
I see at once how structure and technique
Were predetermined by the simple fact
I wrote *Zarathustra* in poetry.
In *Zarathustra* my poetic eye,
Dilated to its visionary bore
(Commandeering the world to see it all),
Was now, by a typical switch of mine,
Forced to focus on specificities,
Each shorn of the wool of mythology,
To get at understanding of my age
And the practical side of government.
I deliberately opposed myself
With an icy dose of prose, of equal
Possibly greater force of energy,
Firing on intellect liberated
From dithyrambic intoxication,
To drive home the intangible vision
The use of poetry had given me.
And I knew the only way to do this
Was in cold, clear, hard, historical prose.
In the event, the way I achieved this
Was to write in a more direct manner
Keeping my intention obvious. Still,
I hung each point, suspended in silence,
To allow me to look up from underneath
To glimpse my own unconscious prejudice
And think, free of the narrative line.

I had, by now, perfected this sly art.
I looked past the sidetracks and wrong-turnings
To get at truth and gain experience
Rid of fervid attitudinising.
I was as consciously hard on myself,
Necessarily cruel to be kind,
As the ardour of my cause demanded.
I was, I now knew, in deadly earnest.
  There's not a single flip word in the book.
Long years of discipline were paying off.
I was down wind of naked energy
Utterly unconscious of my presence.

4

I wanted the origin of evil.
Zarathustra done, was I any more
Than a wild Dionysian poet?
I was an animal contemplating
The last shock waves of dead experience,
Smelting the star of human politics...
I was a cougar crouching to devour
The naked lamb of white energy,
The theological truth about life...
  The roped boats bobbing on the lake, the sun
Yellowing the green moss between the trees,
The belled cows grazing by the waterfall,
Tulips, the breathtaking light of the sky
Shattering the snow-skinned mountaintops, walls
Of granite, massy-hatched with snow, the clouds
Twirling in the exhilarating air,
The shaking lake, the tumbling torrents, firs
Dizzying the waking life of the mind,
The wonderful sense of being alive,
The sheer lucidity of Switzerland,
Of Lake Silvaplana, shone at my feet...
  God himself curls under the living tree

Of knowledge, turning into the serpent
At the end of the divine working week
Creating the mystical universe.
This is the way he takes stock of himself,
Thinking back to himself, to know himself.
It is as the serpent that God knows God
Is out to recover from being God.
The effort of creation exhausts him.
So the devil is God's quilted anvil:
He fashions all sins on him and the blows
Are never heard. Thus, God himself is shot
Of all responsibility and shame.

5

So how exactly did I, in the cold
Light of scientific prose, go about
Making political philosophy?
I imagined a model of the world
Unclouded by the human condition,
Giving myself this dangerous freedom,
As I considered my thinker's duty
To behold our soft blue planet alive
Like an eye beneath the eyelid of space.
The hardest thing a thinker has to do
Is embrace human bestiality
In his reason, without distorting it,
And without being distorted by it.
  Since there is no limit to what we do,
And evil is a part of what we do,
There is no limit to human evil.
If, in practice, evil is infinite,
What possible hope is there for the world?
  The key enigma is morality.
Outside it, birth, copulation and death
Retain no intelligible meaning.
Inside the door, what do they signify?

Who dares to open the moral furnace?
Whose hands dare work in the white heat, dear friend?
 Chinese sages say harmony exists
Serene as the breathing lung of a tree
Beyond good and evil, and I agree
With Chinese sages when they talk like this.
But our dilemma is European.
We are, at the very least, scientific.
Every last step we take must be spelt out.

6

Take Schopenhauer's will, for example.
Isn't it the energy of the world
Before the world has materialised?
Isn't it, therefore, as a part of this,
Its energy *to* materialise?
The energy to materialise
A child, is latent within us at first,
And then, as a part of this, it becomes
The energy *to* materialise
A child. Is Schopenhauer's will, then, sex?
 As sexual beings, we're engaged in
Perpetual creation of matter,
The end weight of which, at any moment,
Is the mass of the people in the world.
What makes us do this? Why the compulsion?
 To articulate the act to the end
Of all the sensations known to the flesh,
And speak beyond, in that dark theatre
Of the spirit, where two human beings
Feel the spirit of a third enter them,
In that physical inner space between
Union, conceived so delicately
Even the violence of love stops there:
Well, in a nutshell, that would be something.
For there, in the act of making people,

Stung by the living touchstone of the soul,
The knowledge of morality begins.

7

To walk with a man in all his glory
Is to meet the man supremely aware
He has the right to create his own values,
And define the world according to these.
The high ground of moral neutrality
Is a luxury he cannot afford.
Detached thinking doesn't come into it.
Whatever helps him is itself helpful,
Whatever harms him is itself harmful.
The man is the nub of morality,
Centre and circumference of the tribe.
He is the tribe's creator of values,
And the tribe respect him for these values.
If he sees something in another man
He recognises as value in himself,
His first instinct is to honour that man.
He knows his high responsibility
And good fortune are one and the same thing.
Neither the good nor the bad concern him.
He is nothing other than the thoughtful
Guardianship of the contented tribe.

8

The sun shines on the green leaves of the trees.
Discreet animals go about their lives.
He contemplates the surrounding dangers
His tribe, or society, least suspects.
He is the grave dilation of the care
Those who put their trust in him most assume.
His instinct coops the tender and infirm,
The newborn and the old, not from pity,
But from the simple fact they all adhere

To his radiant plenitude and strength.
This is how it is. And if he pities,
This is in addition to his power
To legislate the safety of the tribe.
He's nothing but the top and pyramid
Each constructs by consenting to the whole.
It is inconceivable to any
He values weakness more than strength. The more
He values his own strength and eminence,
The better chance his tribe has to survive.
This is the man, the animal that man
Is, in his instinctive nobility.

9

And yet there's more to him than this. Much more.
Above all, he is a man of power,
Distinguished in his looks by his power
To overpower power in himself.
He knows when to speak or remain silent,
Equal in dignity with the discourse.
Like light over rock he dawns on himself,
Setting his range of thought in perspective.
This command of himself delights his colleagues,
Who know how hard such self-discipline is.
When he describes how to take pleasure
In pleasure his colleagues find so difficult,
His laws exchange self-indulgence for strength
To enjoy pleasure unconstrained by it.
He educates men to self-mastery
By revealing how the self-slaved enslave
Those multiple mirror-images of themselves,
Right down to the last starving family,
Until they worship the same slave-master,
The blind unconscious self, which he commands.

10

He knows the corruption of fallible men
Is the normal course of events. Disgrace
Is the common end of the miracle.
Why? The usual answer is pity
For others, never excluding oneself.
'Why is life so full of meaningless pain,
And the suffering of the innocent?'
Reaction breeds resentment, arousing
The latent instinct to revenge, to kill
Men, women, even if only oneself.
As when self-pity convinces a jake
To murder his family, on the grounds
It refuses to recognise his pain.
Or when pity for tribal conditions
Persuades a chief to murder his neighbours
To improve the lot of his starving tribe.
But, by and large, it's a drawn-out affair
We conduct with ourselves over the years.
And because we take pity on ourselves
So slyly, we are the last ones to know.
To justify our slow decline from grace
We draw on any product of the mind,
This reason, that experience, this fact,
To embed it over and against life.
But the truth is, the miracle of life
Is not explained by such sly petulance,
Now lit up, as though on a giant screen,
By the imagination of the man.

11

The more noble the man, the more he feels
Pity for the suffering of others,
Never excluding himself, till, at last,
The more nobly, the more deeply he feels
The all around and everywhere of pain,

The more he is certain to avenge himself
On the spectacle by killing someone,
Even if it's only his self-knowledge.
The more he grasps reality, the more
He is bound by his own heart to pity
The terrifying clamouring of hands
Thrashing the water white where no help comes.
For this is the place the noble man drowns,
Too, swamped by the vision of his pity.
He holds up the vision as he bellows,
'Justify this, you bastards, if you can,
I would rather die with the innocent!'
Those of us who stood with him on the shore
Know that his death proves nothing about life,
Except that his pity was not enough.
Pity is the bait which draws out murder
In man, the more so the nobler he is.
The truly noble feel the greatest pain.
We can almost read off order of rank
In terms of pain the noble man suffers
Ascending his tall career. For profound
Suffering ennobles. It separates.
There, alone at the top, the noblest soul
And just compassion, come into their own.
For from the top, channelled down through power,
Compassion achieves its noblest value:
The Roman Caesar with the soul of Christ.

12

Our man both wants and knows how to honour
The inner glow magnificent in men
More than the gleam which glorifies the gold
And vermilion mountainside in nature.
He respects old age, the spark still burning;
Men, women, children; the old traditions;
And relishes the ancestral stories.

His gratitude concentrates his respect
Glimpsing the artifice of men in file
Reverencing the spirit of the past.
He sits, devoted, to behold the laws
Those who've gone before him fought to secure;
Falling to his knees, when alone, to pray.
He abhors everything supercilious,
Vain, ignoble, forcing such men to bow.
For him, there is no greater privilege
Than the opportunity to venerate
Those who arouse his need for reverence.
His long apprenticeship strove for this end.
The tramp he observes reading *The Bible*,
Unkempt, disreputable, and alone
In an empty church, turning the pages
He hallows with the touch of his fingers,
Arouses exactly the same passion.
Whereas the self-elevated elite
Pompously parading draped cathedrals
Who lack all genuine humility
Disgust him with their lack of reverence
And their shamelessness counterfeiting it.
Their self-satisfied eyes and hands insult
Each mum object they touch, lick, or fumble,
Lip-serving the chaliced Holy Ghost.
Nobility of taste is more among
The bronzed peasants harrowing the mountainside
Than that newspaper-reading demi-monde
Of fops, cultural philistines, and frauds,
Who have forgotten how to revere life.

13

Within his circle of respected peers,
The depth of each commitment in the mind
Reaches to the very edge of honour.
Such value breeds the brotherhood of trust

Of death before defeat, exacting war
On all who rob them of their dignity.
And if his peers notice those maltreating
The weak and helpless (indulging caprice
And a mere superior strength of arms)
Then, because they make war from strength, they may
Deploy compassion to obliterate
The corrupt people inflicting the pain,
Whereas, without strength, they suffer it too.
His characteristic as a person
Who works in a hierarchy of rank
Is that he rarely feels himself a function
Of the state, crown, or commonwealth he serves,
But is its embodiment and meaning,
Its final justification and cause.
Although conscious of being different
From those over whom his rank places him,
He enjoys the feeling of difference
To the extent he knows he deserves it.
His proud and exalted disposition
Shuns any unworthy criticism of those
Over whom he swears to serve with his life.
They in themselves, the citizens, work for
And honour him, because he despises
All who are the opposite of himself:
The mean, selfish, mendacious, and cruel.
And so, by standing up to their enemies,
He helps the citizens to help themselves.

14

He barbs his wit, enmity, and venom
For those who teach lambs out-philosophise
Wolves, in serious debates about life,
Because they advocate unsullied love,
Reflex selflessness, and sweet behaviour,
As the prime statutes of society;

Whereas the law of their hungry neighbours,
The wolves, advocates barking selfishness,
Hate, and onomatopoeic thunder
Howling for blood on the white mountainside.
  He inculcates the truth that the free man
Is hard, the opposition of the soft man,
Who is, ipso facto, enslaved by thought
At least one remove from reality.
Because he is free in the face of it,
The inhospitality of life stamps
Our man's hard character uniquely hard.
Passive, observing with a steady eye,
Cushioned by neither thinking nor thinkers,
Nor excoriated nor struck dumb by
The obvious monstrosity of things,
He guards the borders of the free free world.

15

This is the place our man parts company
With Charles Darwin and the naturalists.
Such biologists note the way things are,
But our man observes observation too,
Including himself noticing the fact.
And he notes how 'biological law'
In its eagerness to divine our source
Glosses over moral philosophy
With all the delicacy and panache
Of muddy boots over a bridal suite.
  Steered by the fierce Muse of Philosophy,
His mind set firmly on the target
Of why there are any targets at all,
His eyes take in the miracle of life.
He considers the origin of facts,
The scattered atoms of the universe,
As, like the people's God, the whole coheres.
  Now he conceives moral philosophy,

Impregnated by the stark fact of life.
In time, the observation of motion,
Which is, the movement of the universe,
The active miracle of life itself
Inscribes the vision of philosophy.

16

Now the moral philosophers arrive
To populate his studied consciousness:
The conclusion-jumpers, the question-mark
Leap-froggers, the cupboard-lovers, the shrill
Peccadilloërs, the snazzy cacti,
The web-weaving dust-catchers, the needle-
Threading hoaxers, the fool's gold chatterers,
Warblers, periwinklers, trumpet-blowers,
Nubile infantilists, axe-grinders,
Educated bores, the plain uninformed,
Language scramblers, show-offs, bigots, the daft,
Fools, fakes, flatfoots, the bees-in-bonneters,
Periphrastics, the obsessed, duds,
Money-munchers, clubbers, moaners, forgers,
The Nothing Brigade, stool prophets, headlice,
Haters, heart-snuffers, simple-minded asps,
And the deep-throated, camel-swallowing gnats.
When soft men or the biologists reign,
These are the philosophers of the age.
Decadence sets in. The bonds and constraints
Of the ancient discipline are broken.
The illusion of welcome in the world
Entrances all but the severest minds.
And as for them, they citicize the moon,
Enchanted by disenchantment with life.

17

The universal decadence of mind,
Like the abracadabra of magic

Enrapturing a crowd's intelligence,
Creates the tropical hot-house effect
Of multiplex, arm-convolving hydras,
Roof-piercing beanstalks, harlequin tigers
Snoozing, zig-zagging bamboo, bats spitting
Red tongues of fire, pink spiders poisoning
Ostreperous toadstools, whose howls arouse
Glass monkeys, albino trees, boozed lizards,
Pinstriped cougars, blinking watermelons,
Y-shaped snakes, twin-eating twins, crooning clones,
Studious grass, eloquent tendrils, leaves
Applauding ballerina elephants,
Statuesque giraffes reciting poems,
Dead drunk stones, as each phantastic spirit,
Perfectly adapted to its culture,
Preaches us its moral philosophy.
In short, the philosophers of muddle,
The politicians of the middle road,
The mediocre, come into being.

The Dream of Intelligence:10

My books were not exactly best-sellers.
In its first year *Human, All-Too-Human*
Sold one hundred and seventy copies.
Beyond Good and Evil did little better.
I gave it to a Jewish publisher,
Credner, who accepted it straight away;
But Schmeitzner, who'd published *Zarathustra*,
Wanted it too, yet wouldn't publish it.
Litigation started. I decided
To pay for the costs of printing the book myself.
I hoped, by selling three hundred copies,
To cover the bill, but within a year
Only one hundred and fourteen copies
Had been sold. I was forced to admit
Reaction to my work was negligible.
  I wrote to my sister Elizabeth
How my career as a writer so far
Had cost me not less than 3000 francs
In printers' bills, but had yet to earn me
Any money at all in royalties.
  I survived on scraps of comfort. My friend
Von Gersdorff wrote, on reading my new book,
'I bless you for being able to live
As a philosopher.' I wrote by return,
'Seldom has a letter caused me such joy.'
I understood the triumph he implied.
The Danish critic, George Brandes, relished
My 'aristocratic radicalism.'
But despite the long list of books to my name
I was virtually unpublishable.
I felt marginalised, suicidal.

I wrote to a friend I wanted to die.

2

Now more than ever before, the horror
Of the origin of evil haunted me.
I ceased to look for the cause of evil
Beyond the world, charmed by theology.
Nor was I any longer to be seduced
By the beauty of the Blind Goddess, justice.
I looked instead at concrete conditions
In which judgements of value first arose.

3

And therefore I declared war on Plato,
Arch-forger of values the Christian
Ecclesiastical establishment
Used to break men with for two thousand years.
Because Christianity is Plato
For the people, behold his best-known face!
Racked by his metaphysics of the Good,
Tension had reached such a pitch in Europe
No perspective obtained. The Good was shelved
In a sphere of glass, purified spirit
Out of the reach of the hammer of evil.
Frustration was infinite, but the grip
Of human desire for Christ's perfection,
The Platonic Good, bound men in holy chains
Inspired by imperial Roman law.
Attempts were made to relax the tension
By the casuistry of Jesuits
And the democratic enlightenment,
But the fact was, domination by Good
Enchanted human imagination
To such a degree the subtler tyrants
Envied the pretty principle employed:
'We know in our hearts how evil we are.

Therefore, O God, to make life bearable,
Direct the light of our minds to the Good
To offset the torture of self-knowledge.'

4

At this point, may I introduce my guide,
Meister Eckhart of the Middle Ages,
1260 to 1327,
Who, in the translucent way of mystics,
Says, 'I ask God that he rid me of God.'?
As we tramped on the slopes through the rare air
Of my giddying imagination,
He held my arm, he steadied my reaction,
As the mountains dropped away – and drew me out.

5

My declaration of war was over
Nothing less than the value of morals.
Earlier, I'd been forced to take issue
With Schopenhauer on this explosive point.
My great teacher had valued compassion
To such an extent he'd projected it
Onto the blue sky and deified it.
  Compassion became his lens to value
In comparison with which, heartless life
(A tunnel of stomachs eating each other
In the dark, copulating as they feed
And die in fresh copulating stomachs,
The tunnel walls a richly sensitive thick-veined
Throbbing gut devouring all unnoticed)
Was the absolute opposite of this.
  Because of his belief in compassion,
Which he would not give up at any price,
He was obliged to vilify life
To remain an honourable thinker.
Like the Buddhists he *was* honourable,

And so, like them, having no other choice,
He was forced to conclude life worthless.
  New buddhists, the European Nihilists,
Were coming into being, an event
Caused by a widening belief in this
Moraliser of compassion, which drew
Even philosophers out of their minds
And made them preach, refuting blameless beasts
Chewing at large in the astonished dusk.

6

The time had come, I saw, to dislodge this
Block about the value of compassion.
How are values made? In what conditions,
What circumstances, are they established?
I set out to explore the forgotten,
The unconscious, mind-breaker of values,
Which, like a press, lay buried in men's minds.
  But not only there. Scholarship had taught me
A better method of digging it up
Than Doctor Paul Rée's (of gazing around
Haphazardly into the blue, after
The manner of the English psychologists)
Existed, and could be put to good use.
  Paul knew nothing about the history
Of morals; of the documented; the known;
Of what has in fact existed; in short,
Of the entire, long, hieroglyphic record
Of our moral past, so hard to decipher.
This was unknown to him. But he'd read Darwin...
  The more I advanced the stranger I felt.
The ground was so pristine, so untrodden,
I thought, 'No one has been here before me.'
And so I encountered, for the first time,
The hard evidence of value-making –
Articulate bone sticking out grotesquely –

Visible to all who travel this way
Crossing the mental deserts to the halls
Of the fossilised records of language.
There, in manuscript, in the printed word,
Guarded as priceless by staunch archivists,
Lay the unmistakable evidence,
But never looked at in this light before.
Far from substantiating Nihilism,
Or any other moral attitude,
The record shows how all are tiny peaks
And troughs the tireless seizmographic pens
Ink from the tremors of the mind-breaker.

7

The first thing I discovered was the true
Etymological significance
Of the word Good in the found languages
Stored in antique scripts and hieroglyphics.
I saw the true meaning of all of them,
Whichever way I turned, spun me around
The same conceptual transformation.
Something astonishing was happening.
I saw there was one organic taproot,
One unanimous ideogram:
Of a person's place in society
Among the nobility; to give one,
And only one, original meaning
(In a strict, sociological sense
With no moral connotation at all):
Of aristocratic and noble soul.
So that which had in the first instance meant
'Of aristocratic and noble soul',
And been fixed in the imagination
As a term of simple definition
To define someone from this social class,
Had, through the popular shorthand of use,

And the slow accumulation of time,
Transformed from the concept 'of top rank'
Into our definitive moral word.
   And this ran parallel with another,
In which the words *common, plebian, low,*
(Names for someone's place in society
In a strict, sociological sense
With no moral connotation at all)
Were, through the popular shorthand of use,
And the slow accumulation of time,
Transformed from the concept 'of bottom rank'
Into our next most moralistic word.
   Bad meant with common or plebian soul,
With a dispossessed or low-ranking soul.
Bad described someone's rank. There was, as yet,
No inculpatory implication.

8

We evolve from our infancy through words.
And as we grow in science we discern
Intelligence permits us to say things
Are other than they are. We discover
The faculty for casting aspersions.
We call a cat a cow, a chair a bed,
A woman a snake, a man a vermin,
Sensing conscious delight in the power
Of turning something into something else.
   And so, at last, to suit our hidden ends,
We cast aspersions on reality.
Of necessity, we must be at war
With the truthful artisans of language.

The Dream of Intelligence: 11

What is the origin of the evil
Who operate outside morality?
What is the origin of decadence?
Those who've survived insanity maintain
The sourest motive in the human soul
Derives from that most radical torment,
The knowledge of being absent from God.
  We feel our poverty, we feel our rage,
Separate as we are, while God usurps
The boundless universe of his absence.
We live diminished. We see (through tears) we are
Nothing more than meat, an unimportant
Even trivial event, God permits
Having made, to be eaten alive, detached
From our agonies, our trite miracles,
Assembling the jawbones of our predators.

2

Once out of the tender dawn of our love
For our heavenly father, who made us
Flesh of his flesh, blood of his blood, we feel
Embarrassed by his inhumanity,
Wide-eyed at the immensity he's quit.
  The Greeks might call this hubris, but the truth
Is simpler: We have too much self-respect
To worship a God who's abandoned us.
Hubris doesn't come into it. We feel
Tortured to inhabit a universe
Of merely animal pain. We are ashamed.
We are the orphans of light, the dark children
Of the only divinity there was,

Our heavenly father, almighty God,
Begotten, shunned, dumped, betrayed, forgotten,
Forced to take a moral lead on his stand.

3

Torture is the word and torture the thought.
For in a society, which loves God
Who long ago abandoned it, there is
Nothing left to counter the suspicion
The absolutely irredeemable
Meaninglessness of human suffering
Cries out to be worshipped, to become God
In place of the God who's abandoned us.
This is the point on which we stake our souls.
This sets us apart from the status quo.
God has become too subtle. We don't see
Why we should worship a divine being
Who claims to redeem our pain in person,
But not within human understanding.
This God is too subtle for his own good.
How can we expect people to believe
A God we cannot understand ourselves?
The God we worship is much simpler:
The absolutely irredeemable
Meaninglessness of human suffering.
This we have set above kings, above law.
This is the foundation of our motive.
Torture is the word and torture the thought.
There is no God but pain for this is sure.

4

To mitigate the torment of our lives
And shun the shameful habit of pretence,
Our first duty is to our dignity.
We used to weep indoors. We used to swear
'I'm happy' as we chatted, even though

We'd wept inside for more than twenty years.
Why did the inexplicability
Of gratuitous suffering inflict
Such refined torture on our intellects?
Was it because our dignity was pierced
By a sense of its own irrelevance,
Which crushed our self-esteem? When God looked out
– An energy far too mysterious
To be baffled by ourselves – he saw through
The sum total of human affliction,
Like a light shining through a dusty glass.
  We are nothing but our limitations.
We owe it to ourselves to do better
Through the power of action. We will will
Extirpation of gratuitous pain
From the body politic. *We* will will,
Let alone the vanishing-act of God.

5

Just as sex sparks the driving force of life,
So it compounds the agony of those
Who recognise all who are born must die
Yet cannot resist the impulse to love.
The sexual instinct first seduces,
Then subverts, knowledge of mortality.
  Dragged indoors, undressed, our minds enraptured,
Nothing except the molten goal of love
Lives on. The dread, the horror, and the grief
Life conceived is heir to are censored out.
No advance is made. The same old story.
Birth, copulation, and death reproduce
The rigid structures of society,
The very thing which silences our pain.
  Enshrined at the head of society,
The idea of the Good perfects itself
Through ever-ascending hierarchies.

Unable to live with this sham ideal,
We take over the high philosophic
And ascetic models as ours by right.

6

What is the origin of the evil
Who operate outside morality?
What is the origin of decadence?
Those who've survived insanity maintain
The sourest motive in the human soul
Derives from that most radical torment,
The knowledge of being absent from God.
We feel hostile, peculiar, withdrawn.
We've no time for sensual dalliance.
We suspect sex. We suspect the senses.
We aim to establish seriousness.
Life as we find it is quite worthless.
Animals swallow animals alive.
Men murder men for profit and power.
Volcanoes, hurricanes, earthquakes devour
Human beings as soon as look at them.
We feel a duty to recreate life
And make a world we can love and respect.
How can this be doubted? Who doesn't feel
Disgusted and resentful to be born
Into the toothwall of an open throat
As echoes of our loving father fade?
Who doesn't feel disgusted to be born
To be abandoned? Therefore we will build
An open highway to a better place,
A better world, where we invent the rules
And butcher those who try to butcher us.

7

How sweetly we despise the common fools
Who used to run our lives, the noble souls,

Who put their trust in God – whose predators
Discriminate between their running legs
With equal relish, while, on running sores
They are themselves consumed by hungry maggots!
  God's laws disgust us. How we pity those
Who pity us our strict malevolence.
We stuck it out. We paid the outrageous price
To live like God, in open rebellion
With everyone and everything that lives.
And damned the inanimate with contempt.
  Contempt alone is right, although we know
How wrong, corrupt, and vile it really is.
But that's the way to live, to stamp the stamp
Of absolute contempt on life and death.
I stamp the authority of disgust
On every thought and action I perform.
The world deserves the insult, pure contempt
Even for that which makes it beautiful.
What feeds on us, repudiate. We'll pay
Whatever price we must to stay alive,
Even on the edge of infinity.
Why quibble? We are dying anyway.
  Thus suicide is the ultimate proof
The resentment we have cultivated
Triumphs over death. For, kept in reserve,
The sting in the tail of our policy,
Immolation consecrates the body
The soul has known, a Viking king drifting
In a burning boat to the sea, redeeming
What God forsook, ridiculed, and foreswore.
  So, although I am rotten to the core,
The true copyplate of God's decadence,
I do at least possess the self-respect
To admit I'm corrupt, to despise death,
And honour my defiance to the end.

8

The popular malcontents of the state
Sensing alternative law, recognise
Just how disgruntled and bereft they are.
Now it is, at precisely the right time,
The rottenness within myself breaks out
Like a contagious disease, infecting
Even the nobler souls, who've no defence
Against the genius of decadence.
   Soon we head the flocking herds of people
Whipped by our slick philosophy of hatred
We ourselves alone comprehend and spread.
No joy is greater than to witness how
The good themselves succumb (all but the best)
Like cattle, like bulls weak with a virus.
We watch them toppling, the moral giants
Who roared and bellowed on the godly plain,
Who now serve us with equal violence,
The intensity of the fury loosed
A most prodigious psychopathic rage.
A kind of rabies of the mind sets in.

9

Once the glory of man outside himself,
The metaphysical authority of God
Has been replaced by science and reason
And the daring of the enlightenment.
God, the supreme authority, buried
In the hinterland of the unconscious,
Withers, like the gods, to an antique myth.
   God is dead. And in the gap created,
A new metaphysical absolute,
Our just contempt for God (the opposite
Of God's contempt for us) now clubs its way
To the utmost seat of state. God is dead,
And in the gap our sense of pain prevails.

10

So who are we? And how did we become?
Because we were failures; because we lost
Every battle we pitched against success
But lacked the courage to sustain the war;
Because we were envious of talent
And jealous of significant success;
Because we were squashed by the heights of life
And the sense of impossible distance;
Because we conspired to take out revenge
On life we were damned never to possess:
It was a godlike pleasure to institute
The vile hypochondria of failure
As our political platform, to make
A name for ourselves as the voice of failure.
  I myself personify the saviour,
The chief, the shepherd, the redeeming voice,
Striding before them like an animal.
Improving on God, leadership demands
I gratify historic grievances.
  I am the ascetic priest of the mind.
It is the easiest thing in the world
To exploit the innocence of service.
Those who most exact service from others
Are the most innocent in this respect.
Civil servants, those in the professions,
Politicians and the military,
The more they exact, the readier they are,
With a force like me, when they see me coming,
To lick my boots, dogs craving the harness.
  I am the high priest of the psychopath.
Because my aim is the status of God,
And the people know it, I inspire them
To the skies of limitless achievement.
The ghosts of past failure are laid to rest.
With the irrational self-sacrifice of love,

Their committees now both trust and fear me.
I have become their tyrant and their God,
Their insane compulsion, but their support.
For I am more reliable than God.

11

I am myself the monster I inspire
Of human meditation. Out of fire
I forge my radiant ferocity
Fusing the bear, the tiger, and the fox.
I laugh at the technology of God,
The old drones fumbling at the archetypes.
I stroll among God's works with all the weight
And upright seriousness of a bear,
Prudent, haughty, swaying, venerable,
An awesome tower of cold dignity
Giving the appearance of one impressed.
But when I speak, misusing trusted words,
I metamorphose my shape to a fox
Trotting the white mountainside to bark on
The cracking back of an icy river.
Herald and mouthpiece of the strange power
Transcending the easy rocks, I announce
Spring to the innocent heirs of God's works,
The tigers of Dionysus flowing
Over the granite peaks, sniffing out the flesh
In monasteries of scatterbrained men.
The art of leaders is to focus pain.
Once and for all I annihilate God,
Our heavenly father, with the relief
Of a man destroying the perfect work.

12

I, the militant German politician,
Set in absolute contradistinction
To Zarathustra (the incarnation

Of German spiritual seriousness)
May also, like him, be called *uberman*,
For I too succour a standing army.
I loosen the hurt souls from their safe moorings
Deep in the dreams of catatonic sleep
Of envy, anger, hatred, and revenge;
And lead them out, through ice, through fire, alive
To the giddying rapture of action.
[The consequence of mental resentment,
Physiological inhibition
Has many first causes: an injudicious
Emigration to a foreign country;
The bafflement of being half-caste;
The folly of an incorrect diet,
As in the endemic alcoholism
Of the middle ages; defeat in war;
Spiralling inflation; the shock of loss;
The failure of a career; exhaustion,
As in the Parisian pessimism
Of the 1850s; the certitude
Of syphilis, of terminal illness;
Betrayal in love: in short, whatever sucks
The hearts and souls out of men and women
And lays them out prone, flattened, shamed, and trounced
By their sense of inferiority.]
Given back to themselves, they recognise
In flashes of lightning, they've been reborn.
And I know how such aroused emotions
Must climax in orgies of blood-letting!

13

And yet I sense something other than me,
Vaster than the infinite dark of space,
Sets foot in the halls I sit and stare in,
The white palace of God; while my mind,
Observant, brooding, melancholic, sad,

Trapped in the harness of the human form,
Toils to understand its mortality.
Like a fool dimly conscious of wisdom,
I feel baffled – all the more belittled.
This is why I suffer. This is why
I am forced to seek a cause for my pain.
I need an object, a reason, something
To nullify the curse of pain and vent
Feelings of metaphysical outrage,
Feelings of rank inferiority.
Wearing the white mantle of the mystic,
I need to kill, as I am killed, to love.
The anaesthesia which comes with this
Is the only narcotic strong enough
To deaden my spiritual torture:
To kill my pain through the emotional release
Watching other people suffer and die.

14

I am the ancient mighty sorcerer.
And I have built my kingdoms on the Earth
Through the lead I've taken on man's contempt
And disgust for the heartlessness of life.
I've risen above the shock. I have found
Evil a satisfactory response.
Because willing relieves pain, the people
Would rather will nothingness than not will;
And once the people will, but will nothing,
There is no limit to the scope of evil.
And I have built my kingdoms on the Earth
Where no one winces at the sight of pain
But thirsts for it, crying, 'More pain! More pain!'
We inflict for the emotional release
Watching other people suffer and die.
The cheery inventions of hell itself
And the pleasures of the torture chamber

Now stand in my service. I am the king
And owner of the European mind.
I am the evil, fanned by a servant,
Kicking the good man crawling to his grave.
   Do not despise me, who despise my spite.
I am, at least, consistent in disgust.
Oppose me, if you dare, but do not cast
Aspersions of superiority.
For I refute your truth. Belief in God?
Art? Science? Scholarship? Philosophy?
Christianity? Please, don't make me laugh,
For these have always been in my power.
Who could endure the full onslaught of truth?
The truth of what I do is also truth.
   When aging saints or youthful statesmen die
And all the world in mourning feels the shock,
'In vain!' the people cry, for death is hard.
'In vain!' the people cry. The virtuous
Can find no meaning in the shock of death.
And even, as you pray, whose relatives,
Whose children, whose loved ones, and whose colleagues
Cling in helpless terror, hit by a freak
Hurricane, flinging their ship on the rocks?
And what do you pray? 'Please, God, make it not so.'?
I hear the good reason out the just God
As mountain villages collapse on high.
Even the evil are not such hypocrites.
Many are the great who have gone before
In clouds of glorious futility.
And I expand into the emptiness
Behind each lonely, cold, and vanished life.
For all are gone where all the dreamers go,
'In vain!' the people cry, for death is hard.

15

Against the imperial genius
Of evil and the will to nothingness,
The wise and percipient state leader
Sets the aristocratic genius
Of the noble will to be human, love,
Poetry, drama, opera, music,
Delight in the senses, science, the beauty
Of autumns in Provençe, reason in rapture,
The fair world of material comfort,
Plenitude, the touchstone of happiness,
The graceful mastery of the martial arts,
The frank candour of animal grace, love
Of life, outliving appearances,
Of life, outliving what may become,
Of life, outliving change and decay,
Of life, outliving birth, sex, and death.
The God which is the God is not the God.

The Dream of Intelligence:12

Nothing is more difficult to discern
Than Christ in reality, the master
Of cruelty in its most inward form.
The face of suffering humanity
He contemplates and is (mutatis mutandis)
Wears an expression of serenity.
The sweatless air of his sweet forehead is
Denial of the bestial in man.
The new militancy of Jesus Christ
Is, in fact, the revolutionary
Seeking to overthrow the bestial state,
Not today, not tomorrow, but in time.
Time and time again, defeated, we see,
His captive, visionary friends in chains,
Pinched by the hot tongs of the torturer,
Dead on the granite of a prison floor.
Calmly, the horizon turning, Jesus
Soothes the standing army of the beaten,
'I did not come to bring peace, but a sword.'
  The constructed war-machine of his words
Reveals a tact of imagination
Possessed by few other forms in nature.
The profundity of the Jewish mind
Taught him how to conquer within the mind.
A new form of spiritual weapon
Had been forged: how to destroy the bestial
And a mere superior state of arms
Not today, not tomorrow, but in time.
  The new law said, 'The wretched are the good,
The poor, the powerless, the dispossessed,
The humble and the sick, the suffering,

The ugly and deformed, the afflicted
Who've learned humility. They are the good,
The blest of God. They are the blest of God.
The powerful and the wealthy, by contrast,
They are the insatiable, the lustful,
The cruel and the evil, the Godless
Who've shunned humility. They are the bad,
The cursed of God. They are the cursed of God
To all eternity. So help me God.'
Out of the suffering of the people,
Out of the hatred, the need for revenge,
A new love grew. Nor did Christian love
Teach us simply to love our enemies.
This was a love so stunningly conceived
It taught us how to conquer them as well,
Not today, not tomorrow, but in time:
The two-thousand-year-old revolution.

2

'What is it about the Day of Judgement
Which so excites my joy, my exultation?
It is the spectacle of kings in boxes
Slatted for the fires; it is the governors
Groaning on the long insult to the stake;
It is the philosophers cowering
In slung fruit; the tragedians shouting
On the rim of the amphitheatre,
As the earth wobbles and smoke and lava
Spew from the chimney of the mountaintop,
Smothering the sleeping town in ashes;
It is the charioteer at the reins
Galloping away through the olive groves,
His armour alight, his hair streamlining
The blaze now engulfed in the burning trees.
I shall not care to minister to these
Ministers of sin. In my potent joy,

I gaze insatiably on all who dared
Vent their fury on the Church of Christ.
What quaestor, priest, or prosecutor knows
More perfect gratification than this?'
Witness Tertullian, the Church Father,
De Spectaculis, 197 A.D.
'In order to make the bliss of the saints
That much more enjoyable (that they may
Thank God the more abundantly for it)
It is given to them to see, undimmed,
The punishments and tortures of the damned.'
Witness Aquinas, the Holy Doctor,
Summa Theologica, volume three.
Edward Gibbon, that wry historian,
Commenting mildly how such passages
Stand in distinct contrast to the Church's
Teaching on forgiveness, said, 'Christians
Were sometimes seduced by resentment
And spiritual pride to delight
In the prospect of their future triumph.'

3

The Romans felt the Jews were something
Like antinature itself: perverters
Of all the values they held most dear;
Weird people, who stood convicted of hate
Of the entire human race; moneymad
Misanthropists; nobodies; pests; lice; rats.
The Jews, by contrast, felt that the Romans
Were an unenlightened, Godless people.
When the Romans boiled over in fury,
They tarred, crucified, and burnt Jews alive,
Street-lamps for the night chariots to Rome.
When the Jewish mind boiled over, it raged
An equal if opposite contempt. Thus,
The Apocalypse of John the Divine.

The Roman was the strong, the noble man;
None stronger nor nobler has existed.
His modus vivendi delights the eye:
Every inscription, every artefact
Serves to remind just how noble he was
Compared to the barbarian estate.
The Jew, by contrast, was the Godly man;
None more spiritual has existed.
Genius of the spirit, in the Jew,
Is something of the first, not the fifth rank.
Let us inscribe six words six metres high,
The golden letters emblazoned over
The bossy arch of human history:
ROMAN AGAINST JEW JEW AGAINST ROMAN.
And my footnote to reconcile the two?
The Roman Caesar with the soul of Christ.
In Rome today, we bow down to four Jews,
Jesus, Peter, Paul, and Mary. Who can doubt
Roman values have been demoralised?
The values of classical Rome did wake,
Grow to prominence, and flourish once more
During the Renaissance – but not for long.
Jewish values reconquered soon enough
During the Reformation – then drove home
Through the French Revolution. Jewish values
Trounced outright the worn classical ideals.

4

What grotesque sexual mutilations,
Like castration and clitorectomy;
What gruesome knifings of the firstborn son
Pledged by his parents to the tribal god;
What cruelties of sacerdotal rite,
Like cutting out the still-beating heart
Of a young woman strapped to the altar:
What pains have not taught the oldest method

Of burning into human memory?
Stoning to death; breaking on cart-wheels;
Piercing with stakes; hack-sawing breasts; horses
Tearing legs apart; clipping the nose off;
Boiling alive in wine or olive oil;
A slow skinning; besmearing with honey,
Then stapling out in the sun for the flies:
What pains have not taught the oldest method
When man feels the need to make memory?
  The origin of a guilty conscience
Is the memory of a broken promise.
To own up to the first promise of all
Is to admit to interdependence;
Or wander in the wilderness alone.
Come the day, we do at last remember
The promises made to society.
Schulden meaning debt gives *schuld* meaning guilt.
If a loss of money is absolute,
Balance is restored by inflicting pain.
  Compensation for a broken promise,
Which cannot be righted, consists, then,
In a warrant for, and a title to,
Cruelty. This is where legality,
The blindfold justice of the law, begins:
The law is the licence to be cruel
In just payment for a broken promise.
From such beliefs, *debtor* and *creditor*,
And all the language of finance, evolve.
How horrified we are to see the law
Glimpsed in the stock-piles of just punishment.
  This area of life has never lost
The smell and bloody hallmarks of torture.
The right to indulge cruelty beslimes
The prison walls closing round each debtor.
The severity of the penal code
Measures the pleasures of the creditor.

The right to inflict pain seems to him godlike,
An enchantment of the highest order,
And a genuine reason to want life.
In court, the judge, in sacred ermine, clasps
(Licked by legal flames) the moral codex
Clad in the iron binding of the law.
This is the secret purpose of the gods,
As in the Aztec human sacrifice,
To vouchsafe the instinct to cruelty.
   And yet, how does the debtor's suffering
Cancel the debt or guilt he's accused of?
It does so because making him suffer
Is in the highest degree pleasurable.
This is a more sophisticated joy
Than the mere lust for revenge. The creditor
Satisfies his anger with the pleasure
Of imposing pain (in one short sharp shock
Or slowly over the years) until he feels
The original guilt has been paid back.
To be repaid in pain achieves a man
A godlike sense of power in his life.
   The refinements of pleasure to be had
Settling debts this way are clearly greater
The lower a creditor stands on the scale
Of the class structure of society,
Presenting the most delicious foretaste
Of the power of life and death to come
When he reaches the top of the social pile.
He feels, like his masters, the exalted
Right of despising with impunity,
The right to treat others as beneath him.
   The bloody amphitheatres of Rome;
The crucifixions; the auto-da-fés;
The costly weddings of a royal pair
Heightened by tortures and executions;
The burning of witches; public beheadings:

When it is time for bad debts to be paid,
The licence to cruelty is the means.
Our sly and subtle love of cruelty
(Spinoza's 'disinterested malice')
Redeems bad debts through the letting of blood.

5

Trapped in the wealth and peace of the just state
Pangs of conscience trouble the soul of man;
(Recall the wood's nocturnal scent of thyme,
The rain-washed trees, the hush of stars, the night
Humming and buzzing on its silent wings).
Bored by reflections on marble walls,
Mocking his nights of trite security,
There is no avenue in history
He looks down, and does not see himself
Greek hero, Scandinavian viking,
Roman, Arab, German, a Japanese
Prowling at night, torching tents, plundering,
Raping, laughing, slaying the naked, free.
He sees his luminous forbears at work
Inside the masks of civilization.
His mind begins to suffer from itself.
His instinct to cruelty finds no outlet
Inside the strict discipline of the state.
Yet nor would he hurt the hair of a child.
So he becomes an artist, one whose mind
Channels inwards, channels his cruelty
On all the suffering he finds within,
To impose eternal form on chaos.
He burns his will, his passion, his contempt,
His denial and his hatred of life,
Into the very fabric of his soul;
Which, reflected back, reveals in his work
All the destructive forces he's survived.
'What does not destroy me makes me stronger.'

This is the artistic labour of the age,
To take the hateful content of our lives,
And turn it into everlasting proof
Of what we are, through which we are, redeemed.

6

The creation of the Christian God
Is the work of the artist's faculty.
Because the apparatus of the state
Prohibits him being a beast indeed,
He inflicts bestiality of thought
On himself instead – and Holy God is born.
He turns the human being of himself
Into bestial flesh – and holy spirit:
The bankruptcy of man redeemed by God.
Only with a God so pure, so holy,
Can he be certain of his worthlessness.
The genius of Christianity
Is to invent a God who pays our debts.
The creditor sacrifices himself
Out of love, out of love for his debtor.
The work of the Greek artist is nobler.
To him, the bestial in man *is* godlike.
Nor does he rage against it, nor turn it
Into a proof of profound worthlessness.
The Christian God serves to justify God,
Off-loading the bestial onto man.
The Greek God serves to justify man,
Off-loading the bestial onto God.
And the God he chooses is Dionysus.
Such a beast of a God takes on himself
Not the right of eternal creditor,
But, what is nobler, eternal debtor.
The Christian redeems by forgiving sin;
The Greek, on the contrary, redeems God
By acknowledging His eternal guilt.

By acknowledging the truth of the evil
Of the Dionysian guilt of God,
My God takes on responsibility
For the conscience of the European soul.

7

I sing the philosophy of Dionysus,
The reason-melting power of the heart.
In practice, of course, it is typical
Of philosophy, throughout its history,
That such respect for beauty *and* horror,
Such love for creation *and* destruction,
Such veneration, *because of love*, for life,
Is the one thing philosophy abhors.
  It is this very point, nevertheless,
Which is the vital distinguishing mark
Of Dionysian philosophy:
This love, which foresees pain and violence,
Yet still concurs with life; this love, which looks
Profoundly into horror as it is,
And joy, to redeem them as they are;
This love is *the wisdom of tragedy*
The God Apollo called Dionysian.
Plato used Socrates like this, to forge
A semiotic of the holy life.
  I have found my life, and now I live it
In the one hope of saving my own soul,
And all afflicted people, who, like me,
Know what it is to be doomed. Redeemed by art,
The science of religion, and the love,
Erupt full-grown, Sweet Music, lift your soul
Out of the flames and ashes of damnation
Ruptured at last of its most precious gold.

PART FOUR

THE AWAKENING

Flat 3, Fourth Floor,
6, Via Carlo Alberto,
Turin,
Italy.

3rd January 1889
7.00 a.m.

CHAPTER 1

Nietzsche Waking In His Bed

Was that a cockerel I heard? Ah, the darkness. How I love the darkness, the perfect darkness, imagination stilled.

What was that? A cockerel? Only the darkness. I see the dreams are over. No more wine, the Chinese poet said. Am I awake?

Oh, the tolling of the bells in Röcken now/Shall I forget them, Leonard? Shall I forget/... What was that? Bong! bong! bong! I am awake. That Franciscan Priory is a pain. Not only every hour, but every quarter of an hour. Bong! bong! bong! bong! That makes it seven.

I like the Priory in Via Garibaldi. It's the idea of there actually being something called sanctuary that I find so funny. I see it now, the Gothic gates shielding the green lawns, and those fascinating under-arches luring one inside... If it wasn't for the people.

Ah, I must be getting old. At 44 and a couple of months? No, it's not that. It's cynicism, and the dying echoes of that giant, European Nihilism. I must be more composed. There can't be long now. The symptoms have got much worse. I've felt them, like the movements inside a pregnant woman. God knows I'm ready. No one could be readier. Nor is it a shame to die, leaving my books behind me – on my grave.

Where red roses will blow forever. What chance of that? Oh, just Romantic courage raising its ugly head again. Shots! Did I hear shots? Probably. And now the other bells. Bong! bong! bong! A different time this time. Really, it's absurd, isn't it? Two Christian churches in the same street, here in Turin, and they can't even agree on what time it is. It's as bad as the Greek Orthodox and Roman Catholic calendars setting Easter weeks apart. Who's fooling who? That's what I'd like to know. And why is time so important?

Is time movement? And my soul is still.

I'm going mad. Don't worry. The antelope, brought down by lions' claws, has more to do than worry. For I remember Silka, whom I loved, boy that I was, head full of Latin. Silka was my muse, not so much Lou Salomé, with that affected 'von' in her name. Silka had dignity, a born aristocrat hacking it in a brothel. Ah well, she's dying too, I suppose. Just like me. Regrets? I doubt it. But didn't she think with her body? It's the curse of my work I think so much with my head. But then, I was a philosopher, wasn't I, and philosophers think with their bodies, don't they, when they're putting down words? Putting down words like Silka touches.

Am I mad already? I think not. There's still the business of the letter to Athens. I may be struck down today, but I may recover. You can't tell with syphilis, until the case is clear. I wouldn't say I live in hope. I'm really not a fool anymore. Yet somehow it seems just that the letter should be sent. After all, even a day teaching philosophy in Athens would save something from the abyss, be a godsend. I've been writing in retreat for too long. I was always a gifted teacher. I had the knack of making fools love knowledge. No surprise. I was a fool myself.

I believed – well, what did I believe? That God was in His Heaven. That help would come. That thought would think. And here I am, waking up from the ashes of my dreams, ready for insanity and death. What crude self-recognition! What trite humiliation! I loved my work. I loved my job. I loved Wagner, so help me. Yet I never thought I'd be pulverized by the mechanical brutality of circumstances, caught, crushed, crucified, during the most tender act of sex itself. I was naïve.

I was wrong. It is the all of life, not the part, which is sacred. Likewise, horror may be an explanation for a part, but not all of it. The reason for horror is the reason for anything. There is no discontinuity in nature. And yet all of life is a part of every part. No solace this, just dying.

I had the courage of my faults. Which were many. I loved too much, for one thing, but didn't show it. I was the hurricane beyond the mountain, suspected but unseen. For no one saw me. The unrequited lover! Or those who did fled. It has to be said I'm sorry I never saw old Stringer again. I loved the pragmatic bastard. He's probably dead of syphilis himself by now.

And what of syphilis? Only the danger of existence. Only the cat snoozing in front of the hurrying mouse. There is nothing mysterious about it. The worms of syphilis must work this one out too. No one gets a free ride. There is the question of thinking.

CHAPTER 2

Getting Up And Getting Dressed

I had the best of everything. What, shots again! Never mind. The best schooling, education, professors, luck. And sex, though little, enough to last a lifetime. And what is the meaning of it all? Is that my shirt? I fancy that tie. Let's be courteous, ceremonial, even a touch of the dandy. What does it matter? The meaning of it all? I ask you. What equation equals torment? How much is suffering worth? Did I hear someone say something? Was that life speaking? But let it pass. I've done my homework now. Give me Italians, give me Greeks, and that shoe. Let's place ourselves among serious folk. Who know how to love, bend their backs, immortalize Romantic courage doomed. Let's be friendly, like to this sock. Let's brush the teeth of the old stoney-woneys, like the Acropolis for example, like my own teeth for example, and get a bit of living done, not that German dying, that English camouflage, that French bullying, that – oh I forget.

(Looking in the mirror). So this is Nietzsche. Well, you could have fooled me. I could have sworn he was somewhere else. Like his books. Or could it be true mirrors lie? Is that a thought? Call that a thought? What are mirrors? Schopenhauer was a mirror. The mirror of the world. Of all the world. I'm grateful to the old bastard. He taught me to think. Rid me of the old soap bubbles.

Am I getting serious? I doubt it. Seriousness is the same fault as frivolity, only arse-about-tit. God is a smack clever. He works it out his own way. He doesn't need human genius, thanks very much. To teach what? The sphericity of the zero? God is a smack.

My great teacher (Am I dressed? Is there really nothing else to do?) was Meister Eckhart – of the Middle Ages.

That man knew to think. Do I rate him, so, next to the love of Lao Tse? Do I say these things to make them jealous? What else – this bloody shoe – on the edge of

I hesitate, a proud rat. I think if I've done anything, it's dignify the beast. The beast within. I don't know. I guess I loved. Nothing was too much to love. And I loved negritude, hated black being called in question. Like the night, like *The Night Song*. I am dying of immortality. Such things are perfect.

And so I'm dressed.

CHAPTER 3

Walking To The Post Office In Via San Francesco d'Assisi To Post His Application For The Chair of Philosophy In Athens

The beauty of flame is the translucency of insight. I won my spurs. Nice horse! Gee, that lamp-post slipped. Give me the Greeks, the solace of their airs – felicitous pun, that. Give me the Greeks, the strumpet/sacred angel bouzouki. Ah, I have loved the Greeks I hope I know no alas. But less than they me? See, I keep my balance. Wow, the walls are burning. There, there, I touch the lip of you postbox. There, there. Be gentle, wall. *POSTED YOU MESSAGE.* Well, now? Turn around old chap. There's the future to face. Don't make Nietzsche laugh. Immortal laurels to be won. For I can dance and I can sing. For I can laugh.

Not far to go. A few paces do it. So I am here. The Piazza Carlo Alberto. What a place to meet. What profound gloom disregarded. What ecstasy melts the cobbles. And oh, what horse. Did I see him whip? Come my angel. I shall see you right. (*He touches the horse*). Don't suffer it. (*The horse, pulling a carriage, rears up, stung by the whip of the cabman*). Ah, sweetie horse, you are my beast indeed. (*He embraces the horse's neck*). I shall redeem that whip. (*The cabman whips the horse again, striking Nietzsche's hand as well*). Not to worry horse. The day is done. Goodbye mind you were the best. (*The cabman jumps down, not a little indignant, and moves towards Nietzsche*).

CHAPTER 4

Back In His Flat Under The Care Of His Landlord, Carlo Davide

So be it, friend. And why no wine no music double-cross the antidotes. Of antidotes the sting the sacred formula the Russian girls the shake the potency. What love? What am I doing? It seems so long ago. And now there is only Wagner. What bitter joy! With such as me oops I lost my bal – Wagner is king but king of what? Of Troy! Give me my battlesticks, my hymns. Give me Achilles and the Risen Christ. I loved my father God knows I loved God too the antidote of man and blameless beasts.

CHAPTER 5

Playing The Piano Waiting For Franz Overbeck, His Faithful Friend

See it's easy, music. Wagner the ham thought to think it difficult. Old fool. I am entranced. The entrance into the world is to be entranced. Felicitous pun, old chap. No one listens. More's the madness now I am.

What I am   the igneous   the ignited   the
Ah give it a rest   the crucified   done done done

*

CHAPTER 6

Eleven And A Half Years Later

Eleven and a half years later, having spent the rest of his life insane, Nietzsche died in Weimar. His body was taken to Röcken and buried beside his father and his younger brother Joseph. In time, red roses were planted.

SEBASTIAN BARKER was born in Gloucestershire in 1948, and educated at Oxford and East Anglia Universities. He recieved a major Arts Council Award in 1976. He has been Writer in Residence in a number of different social settings, and has directed or co-directed five literature festivals. He has published seven volumes of poetry and a documentary novel, and edited eight anthologies. He is currently Chairman of the Poetry Society of Great Britain. He began working on *The Dream of Intelligence* in 1985. Enitharmon Press are bringing out his *Selected Poems: Guarding the Border* concurrently with this volume.